HOUGHTON MIFFLIN

SOCIAL STUDIES
TENNESSEE

Practice Book

....

- ★ **Interactive Summaries**
- ★ **Reading Skills and Strategies**
- ★ **Vocabulary and Study Guide Activities**
- ★ **Skillbuilder Reviews**
- ★ **Map and Graph Practice**

Visit
www.eduplace.com

HOUGHTON MIFFLIN   BOSTON

**UNITED STATES
CIVIL WAR TO TODAY**

Credits
Illustrations: © Houghton Mifflin School Division
Maps: Mapping Specialists, Ltd.
Photography: 118 Courtesy of the Maryland Historical Society.

Printed in the U.S.A.

ISBN-13: 978-0-618-96508-3
ISBN-10: 0-618-96508-4

4 5 6 7 8 9-1409-15 14 13 12 11 10
4500241329

HOUGHTON MIFFLIN   BOSTON

HOUGHTON MIFFLIN
SOCIAL STUDIES

Contents

Practice Book
iii
Use with *United States: Civil War to Today*

HOUGHTON MIFFLIN
SOCIAL STUDIES

Almanac Map Practice

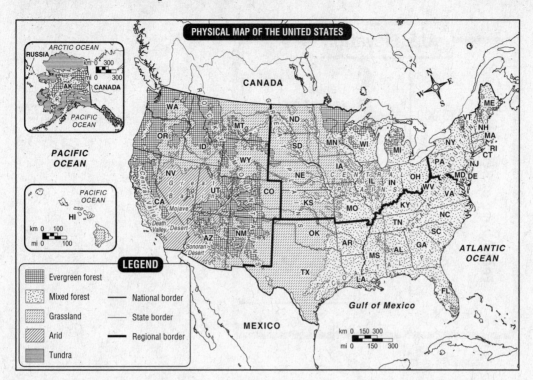

Use the map to do these activities and answer these questions.

Practice

1. Circle the large lake located in the Great Basin.

2. Based on the legend, how would you describe the land of the Great

Plains? _____

_____

3. Is the land in South Carolina arid? How can you tell?

_____

_____

4. Shade the only state along the Atlantic coast that has grassland.

Apply

5. Work with a partner to locate your state on the map. Describe its

land. _____

Almanac Graph Practice

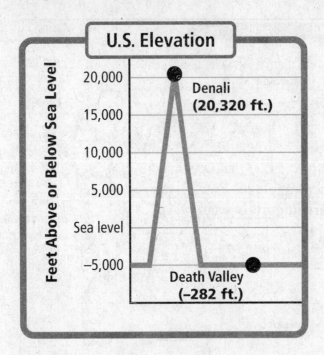

U.S. Elevation

Feet Above or Below Sea Level

- 20,000
- 15,000
- 10,000
- 5,000
- Sea level
- –5,000

Denali
(20,320 ft.)

Death Valley
(–282 ft.)

Practice

1. What is the elevation of Denali? _____

2. Is Death Valley above or below sea level? _____

Apply

3. Use the information below to complete the line graph.

Mountain	Elevation
Mt. Whitney, California	14,491 feet
Mount Le Conte, Tennessee	6,593 feet

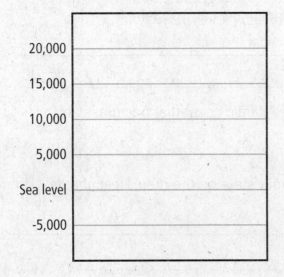

- 20,000
- 15,000
- 10,000
- 5,000
- Sea level
- –5,000

2

Summary: Our Nation's Resources

Geography of the United States

The United States has many landforms. In the East, the Appalachian Mountains stretch from north to south. The Rocky Mountains are in the West. There are wide plains across the center of the nation.

Large rivers from the plains flow into the Mississippi River. This is the nation's longest river. The Great Lakes are on the northern side of the central plains. The Mississippi River and the Great Lakes are important waterways.

The Nation's Resources

The United States has resources all over the country. A resource is something people use to produce goods and services. Renewable resources can be replaced. Fish are a renewable resource. New fish hatch to replace those that are caught. Nonrenewable resources cannot be replaced. Oil is nonrenewable. When it is taken from the ground, no new oil will take its place.

Flow resources can only be used where and when they are found. Wind, water, and sunlight are flow resources that can be used to make electricity.

Capital resources are the buildings, tools, and machines that people use to make goods and provide services. For example, farmers use tractors to grow and harvest corn. Human resources are people who use their skills and knowledge in their work.

Everyone who uses resources has a problem with scarcity. This means that people must choose what they want most. For example, say your class has enough money to buy either books or art supplies. If you choose to buy the books, the opportunity cost would be the art supplies.

Countries make the same kinds of choices. A nation's economic system helps countries decide how people use resources and produce goods. The economic system of the United States is a free enterprise system.

Before You Read

Find and underline each vocabulary word.

resource *noun,* something people use to produce goods and services

scarcity *noun,* not having enough resources to provide for all our needs and wants

opportunity cost *noun,* the thing that you give up when you decide to do or have something else

economic system *noun,* a set of rules that guides the use of resources and production of goods in a country

free enterprise *noun,* a system by which businesses and individuals, instead of the government, answer certain economic questions

After You Read

REVIEW **What is the difference between renewable and nonrenewable resources?** Circle two sentences that tell the answer.

REVIEW **Who is affected by scarcity?** Draw a box around the sentence that tells who has a problem with scarcity.

Practice Book
3
Use with *United States: Civil War to Today,* pp. 6–9

Reading Skill and Strategy

Reading Skill: Cause and Effect

This skill helps you see how one event can be related to another, either by causing it or resulting from it.

Read "The Nation's Resources." What is the effect of using renewable and nonrenewable resources?

Cause	Effect
Fish are caught at a fishery.	1.
Oil is removed from the ground.	2.

Reading Strategy: Predict and Infer

3. Read "Geography of the United States." Then check the best inference.

____ People in the United States live in many different landform areas.

____ Wide plains in the center of the country are high and difficult to climb.

____ People who live in the Appalachian Mountains enjoy vacationing in the Great Lakes.

4. Read "The Nation's Resources." Then check the best inference.

____ When goods are scarce, people enjoy themselves more.

____ Using a lot of nonrenewable resources is good for the environment.

____ A good economic system depends on many kinds of resources.

Vocabulary and Study Guide

Vocabulary

Write the definition of each vocabulary word below.

1. resource _____

_____

2. scarcity _____

_____

3. opportunity cost _____

_____

4. economic system _____

_____

5. free enterprise _____

_____

Study Guide

Read "The Nation's Resources." Then fill in the comparison chart below to compare natural, capital, and human resources.

	Natural resources	Capital resources	Human resources
What are some examples?	6.	7.	8.
What are they used for?	9.	10.	11.

Practice Book
5
Use with *United States: Civil War to Today*, pp. 6–9

Skillbuilder: Review Map Skills

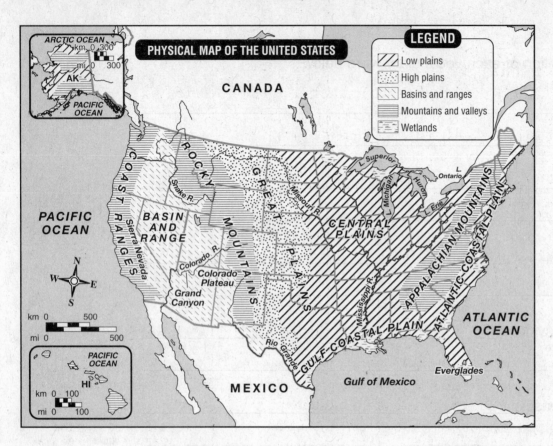

PHYSICAL MAP OF THE UNITED STATES

LEGEND
- Low plains
- High plains
- Basins and ranges
- Mountains and valleys
- Wetlands

Practice

1. What landform surrounds the Mississippi River? _____

2. In what direction would you travel to get from the Atlantic Coastal

   Plains to the Rocky Mountains? _____

3. What type of physical features cover Hawaii?

   _____

4. Approximately how many miles is it from the Grand Canyon to the

   Pacific Ocean? _____

Apply

Look at the natural resources map in Lesson 1. Find the region where

you live. Write the name of your state and two resources that are found

close to your region. _____

Practice Book

6   Use with *United States: Civil War to Today*, pp. 12–13

Summary: Regions of the United States

What Is a Region?

Geographers study regions to learn about different places. The United States is divided into many types of regions. Each region has features that make it different from others. Regions of the United States can be divided by location. The four regions are the Northeast, the South, the Midwest, and the West.

The country can also be divided into regions with similar landforms. For example, the Rocky Mountain region has many steep mountains. The Great Plains region has flat or gently rolling land.

Geographers divide regions by climate, too. Regions in the Southwest get more sunshine than regions in the Northeast.

Regions can also be based on the goods people produce. The Corn Belt in the Midwest produces more corn than any other region. Regions can also be areas where most people speak the same language or share the same customs.

Regions can change. Silicon Valley used to be a fruit-growing region. Now, computers are its main business.

Regions and the Economy

The resources in a region help people decide which crops to grow and which goods to produce. For example, Tennessee's soil and climate are very good for growing cotton, so many farmers in Tennessee grow and sell cotton. If a business makes a lot of one product, it costs less to produce it. Specialization results when people make goods using the resources they have.

Today all regions of the United States are interdependent. People trade with other regions for goods and services they do not have. Trading gives consumers a bigger variety of things to buy. When people in one region decide to produce something, it affects people in other regions all over the country.

Before You Read

Find and underline each vocabulary word.

region *noun,* an area that has one or more features in common

specialization *noun,* the result of people making the goods they are best able to produce with the resources they have

interdependent *adjective,* to depend, or rely, on each other

trade *noun,* the buying and selling of goods

After You Read

REVIEW **What are three kinds of regions in the United States?** Highlight at least three ways geographers divide the nation into regions.

REVIEW **In what way does trade affect what people can buy?** Circle the sentence that tells the answer.

Reading Skill and Strategy

Reading Skill: Draw Conclusions

Sometimes when you read, you have to figure out things that the writer doesn't tell you. This skill is called drawing conclusions.

Read "Regions of the United States." Then fill in the draw conclusions chart below.

Regions are areas that share similar features.	Different regions have different resources.	Specialization occurs when people use their resources to make certain products.

1.

Reading Strategy: Predict/Infer

2. Read "What Is a Region?" Then check the best inference.

   ____ Regions are created by grouping states that are about the same size.

   ____ Nearby states are grouped together as a region because they usually share many characteristics.

   ____ The way that people think about a region never changes.

3. Read "Regions and the Economy." Then complete the statement.

   A region's natural resources often determine _____

   _____ .

Vocabulary and Study Guide

Vocabulary

1. Draw a line connecting the vocabulary word to its meaning.

trade	Focusing on making the best goods with resources you have
region	The buying and selling of goods
interdependent	To depend, or rely, on each other
specialization	An area that has one or more features in common

Study Guide

2. Read "What Is a Region?" Then fill in the blanks below.

One way to study regions in the United States is to group together _____ that are close to each other. Another way to study regions is by looking at similar _____ . For example, the _____ region is made up of flat land or gently rolling land.

3. Read "Regions and the Economy." Then fill in the blanks below.

Each region of the United States uses its _____ to produce goods and services. Tennessee has a soil and climate that are perfect for growing _____. Minnesota and _____ have a lot of iron ore. Some regions _____, or make large amounts of only certain products. Then they must _____ with other regions to get the goods they do not make themselves.

Practice Book
9   **Use with *United States: Civil War to Today*, pp. 14–17**

Summary: People and the Land

How Land Affects People

The land and its resources affect where and how people live. Many people settle in places where they can earn a living. For example, New York City is on the Atlantic coast. It has a good harbor for shipping. Shipping and trade helped the city's economy grow. This economy continues to provide jobs for many people today.

Thousands of people moved to San Francisco, California, when miners discovered gold near there. Stores and restaurants opened to serve the growing number of miners.

Many people settle in places such as Florida and Arizona because they like the environment, which includes pleasant weather. Geography affects how people have fun. People ski on mountains. Other people fish in lakes, rivers, and oceans.

Changing the Environment

The land is always changing. Natural forces such as earthquakes and volcanoes cause sudden changes. Wind and rain can slowly wear away soil and rock. They can change tall, steep mountains to lower, rounded mountains.

People also change the land. These changes affect the environment in both good and bad ways. Building highways makes travel easier, but the land can no longer be used for other things, like farming. Building dams provides electricity, but it changes the wetland environments. Strip mining for coal provides fuel, but it can cause water pollution.

Many ecosystems make up our environment. Each part of an ecosystem affects all the other parts. For example, a lake is an ecosystem that has water, birds, fish, and plants. If the water becomes polluted, it can harm the plants and animals there.

Today, people practice conservation to save our resources. Conservation helps protect the environment and its ecosystems. Using water, gas, and electricity wisely are ways to conserve resources. Protecting wilderness areas, recycling, and passing laws to control pollution are other ways that people conserve resources.

Before You Read

Find and underline each vocabulary word.

environment *noun,* the surroundings in which people, plants, and animals live

wetland *noun,* a moist area such as a swamp or marsh that provides a home for wildlife

pollution *noun,* anything that makes the water, air, or soil dirty and unhealthy

ecosystem *noun,* a community of plants and animals, along with nonliving things, such as soil, air, and water

conservation *noun,* the protection and wise use of natural resources

After You Read

REVIEW **In what way did the geography of New York City help it grow?** What two things helped the city's economy grow? How do these things affect today's economy? Underline two sentences that tell the answer.

REVIEW **In what way does conservation save resources?** What two things does conservation help to protect? Draw a box around the sentence that tells the answer.

Name _____ Date _____

Reading Skill and Strategy

Reading Skill: Categorize

This skill helps you understand and remember what you have read by organizing facts into groups, or categories.

Read "People and the Land." Then fill in the categorization chart below.

Ecosystem	Wetland
1.	2.

Reading Strategy: Predict/Infer

3. Read "How Land Affects People." Then complete the statement.

   The weather and landforms often affect _____

   _____

4. Look over "Changing the Environment." Read the headings. Make a prediction about what the section will be about.

   _____

   _____

   _____

5. Make a prediction about the future of the environment.

   _____

   _____

   _____

Vocabulary and Study Guide

Vocabulary

Solve the clue and write the answer in the blank. Then find the word in the puzzle. Look up, down, forward, and backward.

1. Anything that makes the water, air, or soil dirty and unhealthy _____

2. The surroundings in which people, plants, and animals live _____

3. A moist area such as a swamp or marsh _____

4. The protection and wise use of natural resources _____

5. A community of plants and animals, along with nonliving things _____

E	C	Y	I	H	X	R	F	A	S	O
P	O	L	L	U	T	I	O	N	V	C
L	N	F	H	E	U	N	T	I	K	T
J	S	G	N	T	S	Q	E	W	R	J
W	E	T	L	A	N	D	C	G	H	O
M	R	W	V	G	F	U	O	D	Q	K
Z	V	G	X	J	H	F	S	X	S	U
N	A	C	W	D	O	A	Y	J	L	B
A	T	M	E	I	Y	E	S	K	P	V
Q	I	D	Y	C	R	K	T	B	M	D
C	O	Z	L	B	P	A	E	Z	B	P
E	N	V	I	R	O	N	M	E	N	T

Study Guide

Read "People and the Land." Then fill in the chart below.

How land affects people	How land changes	How people affect the environment
6.	7.	8.

Summary: Tennessee's Regions

Tennessee's Location

Tennessee is located in the Upper South region of the United States. It shares boundaries with eight states. A boundary is the edge of a region. The state is also divided into three regions, or grand divisions: West Tennessee, Middle Tennessee, and East Tennessee.

West Tennessee has a mild climate, a fair amount of rainfall, and rich soil. These conditions allow people in this region to earn a living from farming. One major industry is food processing. Some people manufacture goods such as plastics, automobile parts, and paper goods. Memphis is in the southwest corner of the state overlooking the Mississippi River. Memphis has the largest population of any city in Tennessee. Its location led it to become a major shipping center.

Middle Tennessee

Middle Tennessee stretches from the Tennessee River to the Cumberland Plateau. It includes the Nashville Basin and the Highland Rim. Middle Tennessee has the largest and most varied economy in the state. The Nashville Basin has land that is good for farming. Farmers also raise animals such as cattle, dairy cows, and hogs. Many people work in manufacturing in the Highland Rim. Nashville is located in the Nashville Basin. Nashville has the state's second largest population. It provides jobs in government, business, education, health care, tourism, and the music recording industry.

East Tennessee

East Tennessee stretches from the Cumberland Plateau to the Unaka Mountains. Important natural resources in this area are timber, coal, and zinc. Many people make their living in the timber and mining industries, and in science and technology. The Great Smoky Mountains National Park also provides jobs in tourism.

Tennessee's climate is different in the different regions. One factor that affects climate is the distance from the equator. Elevation also affects climate. Scientists can use a climograph to show the monthly average temperatures and precipitation for a place.

 Before You Read

Find and underline each vocabulary word.

boundary *noun*, the edge of a region

climograph *noun*, a graph that shows monthly average temperatures and precipitation for a place

After You Read

REVIEW What effect has the geography of West Tennessee had on its economic activities? Underline the sentence that tells one way people earn a living because of the mild climate and rich soil. Draw a circle around the sentence that tells how a river affected the economy of Memphis.

REVIEW What are some of the ways people in Middle Tennessee earn a living? Highlight some of the ways people in Middle Tennessee earn a living.

REVIEW What are some of the ways people in East Tennessee earn a living? Draw a box around the two sentences that tell how some people in East Tennessee earn a living.

Practice Book
13   Use with *United States: Civil War to Today*, pp. 26–31

Reading Skill and Strategy

Reading Skill: Compare and Contrast

This skill helps you understand how historical events, places, or people are similar and different.

Read "Memphis," "Nashville," and "Knoxville and Chattanooga." Then fill in the chart below to compare and contrast river locations and early economies of the cities.

Memphis	Nashville	Knoxville
On a cliff overlooking the Mississippi River; A major shipping center	1.	2.

Reading Strategy: Predict and Infer

3. Look over "East Tennessee." Then check the best prediction.

    ____ The land in East Tennessee is good for farming.

    ____ East Tennessee does not have forests.

    ____ There are more miners than farmers in East Tennessee.

4. Read "Climate." Then complete the statement that you can infer.

    Compared to the climate of a northern state such as Maine,

    Tennessee's climate _____

Vocabulary and Study Guide

Vocabulary

Write the definition of each vocabulary word below.

1. boundary _____

2. climograph _____

_____

3. Use each word in a sentence about the lesson. _____

_____

_____

_____

Study Guide

Use the chart to compare West, Middle, and East Tennessee.

West Tennessee	Middle Tennessee	East Tennessee
4. Landforms _____ _____	**5. Landforms** _____ _____	**6. Landforms** _____ _____
7. Crops or Natural Resources _____ _____ _____	**8. Crops or Natural Resources** _____ _____ _____	**9. Crops or Natural Resources** _____ _____ _____
10. Products and Services _____ _____ _____	**11. Products and Services** _____ _____ _____	**12. Products and Services** _____ _____ _____
13. Major City or Cities _____	**14. Major City or Cities** _____	**15. Major City or Cities** _____

Use with *United States: Civil War to Today*, pp. 26–31

Summary: Declaration of Independence

Declaration of Independence

Congress asked Thomas Jefferson and others to write a declaration of independence. They needed a document to declare why the colonies had to become independent of Britain. In this document, Jefferson wrote what many Americans believed about their rights. Jefferson wrote that people have the right to live, the right to be free, and the right to seek happiness. The Declaration explains why the colonies should break away from Britain. It says that people have rights that cannot be taken away, lists the complaints against the king, and argues that the colonies have to be free to protect the colonists' rights. At the bottom of the document, the delegates signed their names.

Importance of the Declaration

Jefferson wrote that if a government does not protect the rights of citizens, people have the right to form a new government. This idea was not new. Jefferson used ideas that John Locke and other English thinkers had written about. Jefferson listed many ways that Britain had not served the colonists. He wrote, for example, that King George had tried to take away rights and force taxes on the colonies. Jefferson showed that the colonists had a right to separate from the king and have their own government.

The Declaration of Independence was approved on July 4, 1776. The Declaration is still important because it says the American people believe in equal rights for all. Today we know that the words "all men are created equal" include everyone: women, men, children, and every race, group, and ability. But in 1776, people's ideas were different. Only white men who owned property had the right to vote. Laws that recognized equal rights of other groups were passed later.

Before You Read

Find and underline each vocabulary word.

declaration *noun*, a statement that declares, or announces, an idea

independence *noun*, freedom from being ruled by someone else

rights *noun*, freedoms that are protected by a government's laws

After You Read

REVIEW According to the Declaration, why did the colonies have the right to their own government? Circle the sentence that tells about how the Declaration explains why the colonists should have rights and be independent of Britain.

REVIEW Why is the Declaration so important to Americans? Highlight the sentence that says why the Declaration is still important.

Use with *United States: Civil War to Today*, pp. 36–39

Reading Skill and Strategy

Reading Skill: Cause and Effect

This skill helps you see how one event can be related to another, either by causing it or resulting from it.

Read "Importance of the Declaration." Then fill in the cause-and-effect chart below.

Britain did not serve the colonists.	1.	2.

The colonists had the right to create their own government.

Reading Strategy: Monitor/Clarify

3. Read "Equality Then and Now." Then tell how you monitored your understanding of the selection.

   _____

   _____

4. Write one section that you still find difficult to understand.

   _____

5. Reread the section you found difficult to understand. Then write a sentence about it.

   _____

   _____

   _____

Practice Book
17   Use with *United States: Civil War to Today*, pp. 36–39

Vocabulary and Study Guide

Vocabulary

Across

3. Freedom from being ruled by someone else

Down

1. Freedoms protected by law
2. A statement that announces an idea

Study Guide

4. Read "Declaration of Independence." Then fill in the blanks below.

   By the 1770s, the American colonies wanted their

   _____ from _____. Congress asked five

   people, including _____ to write a

   _____ to tell why the colonies should be independent.

   Jefferson said that people have certain _____ that

   no one can take away. He wrote that they have the right to

   _____, to be _____, and to seek

   _____.

5. Read "Importance of the Declaration." Then fill in the blanks below.

   Jefferson argued that unless a government protected people's

   _____, people could start a new government. He also

   wrote that "all men are created _____." At the time,

   however, only white men who owned property could

   _____. Eventually other groups, such as

   _____, _____, and

   _____ gained equal rights.

Name _____ Date _____

Summary: The Constitution

A Plan for Government

The Constitution tells us that our government is a democracy. It divides the government into three branches. The legislative branch, or Congress, makes laws. Congress also collects taxes to pay for services. The executive branch carries out the laws. The President is the head of this branch. A new President is elected every four years. The judicial branch is made up of courts. They decide what laws mean and whether they have been followed. Everyone, including the government and its officials, must follow the laws.

Limits on Government

The Constitution includes checks and balances. They keep one branch from becoming stronger than the others. The President makes treaties and chooses judges. Congress can reject these treaties or judges. Congress makes laws. The President can veto these laws. The courts can decide if a law follows the Constitution. A law that is found unconstitutional is no longer in effect.

The Constitution creates a federal system. The three levels of government are national, state, and local. The national government has power over national issues. This includes defense, printing money, the postal service, and trade. State governments have power over local issues. States control education and elections. Both systems collect taxes and set up courts. Federal laws are stronger than state laws. The highest law is the Constitution itself.

Changing the Constitution

The Constitution was written so that it can be changed as the country changes. An amendment becomes law when two-thirds of the members of the House and Senate vote for it. Three-fourths of the states also have to ratify it. The first ten amendments are the Bill of Rights. They protect rights, such as freedom of speech. The tenth amendment limits the power of the federal government. In 1790, the Constitution did not protect the rights of all Americans. People have fought for their rights and won. Today the Constitution gives equal protection to more citizens.

Before You Read

Find and underline each vocabulary word.

Constitution *noun*, our written plan of government

levels of government *noun*, national, state, and local governments

federal *adjective*, a system under which the national and state governments each have certain powers

amendment *noun*, a change to the Constitution

Bill of Rights *noun*, the first ten amendments to the Constitution listing the rights of citizens

After You Read

REVIEW What are the jobs of each branch of the national government? Circle the jobs of each branch.

REVIEW Why did the authors of the Constitution create checks and balances and a federal system? Circle the sentence that explains checks and balances.

REVIEW Why does the Constitution include a way to make amendments? Circle the sentence that tells what happens as the country changes.

Reading Skill and Strategy

Reading Skill: Categorize

This skill helps you understand and remember what you have read by organizing facts into groups, or categories.

Read "Limits on Government." Then fill in the categorization chart below. What are examples of checks and balances assigned to each branch of the federal government?

Supreme Court	President	Congress
The Supreme Court can declare a law passed by Congress unconstitutional.	1.	2.

Reading Strategy: Monitor and Clarify

3. Read "A Plan for Government." Then complete the statement.

   The _____ describes how the United States

   government works.

4. Read "Branches of Government." Then explain how the United States

   national government is divided. _____

   _____

5. Read "Changing the Constitution." Then explain why many Americans
   wanted a Bill of Rights added to the Constitution.

   _____

   _____

Vocabulary and Study Guide

Vocabulary

Across

2. The first 10 amendments to the Constitution listing the rights of citizens

3. A system under which the national government and the state governments each have certain powers

4. A change to the Constitution

5. Our written plan of government

Down

1. National, state, and local are three "levels of _____"

Study Guide

6. Read "Changing the Constitution." Then fill in the outline below.

   I. Main Idea: _____

   _____

   A. A change can be made with an amendment.

      1. Detail: _____

   _____

   _____

      2. Detail: Three-fourths of the states must also ratify it.

   B. The Bill of Rights is a list of amendments written in 1791.

      1. Detail: _____

   _____

   _____

      2. Detail: _____

   _____

   _____

   _____

Use with *United States: Civil War to Today*, pp. 42–47

Skillbuilder: Solve a Problem

Keeping the Rio Grande Clean

The United States and Mexico share a border that is almost 2,000 miles long. About 1,000 miles of this border is a river called the Rio Grande. Over 100 years ago, both countries realized they needed to work together to care for the river. They needed to figure out how to solve boundary problems when the river changed course, and how to use the water.

In 1944, they formed the International Boundary and Water Commission (IBWC) to deal with water power, flood control, and rules that make sure no untreated sewage, or human waste, goes into the river. The United States helped Mexico pay for a new sewage treatment plant. Both nations want to make sure that the water they share stays clean for everyone.

Practice

1. What conflicts were the United States and Mexico trying to resolve?

   _____

   _____

2. What goals did the two countries share? _____

   _____

3. In what way did the United States compromise to make the solution

   work? _____

   _____

Apply

Use the library or the Internet to research a current conflict between two groups in your town or community. Use the steps in "Learn the Skill" in your book to identify the conflict and the goals of each side. Then suggest and evaluate possible resolutions to the conflict.

22   Use with *United States: Civil War to Today,* pp. 50–51

Summary: The Ideals of Democracy

Citizenship

In many countries throughout history, ordinary people have had no role in their government. In a democracy, all people help shape the government. The United States is a democracy that gives its citizens many rights. The Bill of Rights in the Constitution lists some rights, such as the right to speak freely, the right to practice any religion, and the right to a fair trial in court. One of the most important rights is the right to vote. When citizens vote, they help choose their government leaders. At age 18, citizens can register to vote.

Our government protects these rights. The government also protects the rights of all people to be treated fairly in housing and jobs, so that no one can discriminate against them because of religion or race. People who come to the United States from other countries can become citizens through the process of naturalization.

Citizens' Responsibilities

Our government gives citizens freedom and many rights. But citizens have responsibilities to the United States, too. Citizens must obey the law. This helps to keep our communities safe. Citizens must pay taxes. Taxes help the government pay for police, roads, and many other important services. Citizens are responsible for voting. Citizens must take turns being on a jury. Men over 18 years old have the responsibility of registering for the military. Young people have responsibilities, too. They must go to school. Education helps young people make good choices and decisions. This helps them become good citizens.

Our government works hard to make the United States a good place to live. But people need to help our democracy stay strong. Some ways to help are by learning about what is happening in the community, voting, and volunteering. Volunteers help communities in many ways. A strong democracy like the United States depends on its citizens to participate.

Before You Read

Find and underline each vocabulary word.

naturalization *noun*, the process of becoming a citizen by learning the laws of the country and the rights and duties of citizens

register *verb*, to sign up

responsibility *noun*, a duty that someone is expected to fulfill

volunteer *noun*, someone who helps other people without being paid

After You Read

REVIEW At what age can citizens register to vote? Circle the sentence that tells the answer.

REVIEW In what ways can being informed about issues prepare young people to be good citizens? Circle the sentences that tell why education is important for young people.

Reading Skill and Strategy

Reading Skill: Classify

This skill helps you understand and remember what you have read by organizing facts into groups, or categories.

Read "Voting and Other Rights" and "Protecting Rights." Then fill in the chart below. Classify citizens' rights that are protected under the Bill of Rights and by the federal government.

Bill of Rights	Federal Government
1.	2.

Reading Strategy: Monitor and Clarify

3. Read "Citizenship." Then complete the statement.

   _____ are freedoms protected by law.

4. Read "Responsibilities of Young People." Write a question you had

   after you finished reading. _____

   _____

5. How did you answer your question? Answer with a complete sentence.

   _____

   _____

Vocabulary and Study Guide

Vocabulary

1. Draw a line connecting the vocabulary word to its meaning.

responsibility	The process of learning the laws of a country and the rights and duties of its citizens
register	A person who helps other people without being paid
naturalization	A duty that people are expected to fulfill
volunteer	To sign up

Study Guide

2. What is the Bill of Rights? List three items written in the Bill of Rights.

_____

_____

_____

3. How else does the government protect the rights of citizens?

_____

_____

Read "Citizens' Responsibilities." Then fill in the compare-and-contrast chart below.

Responsibilities: adults	Responsibilities: young people
4.	**5.**

Use with *United States: Civil War to Today*, pp. 52–55

Almanac Map Practice

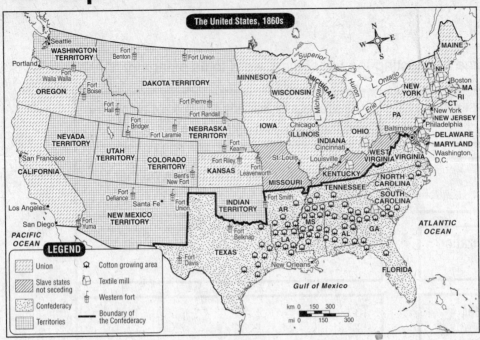

Use the map to do these activities and answer these questions.

Practice

1. Which five slave states did not secede from the Union?

_____

2. Which Union states were the farthest west?

_____

3. On which side of the Civil War were most cotton producers located?

   Most textile mills? _____

   _____

Apply

4. Work with a partner. Read about free states and slave states in "Compromises in Congress" in Lesson 3 of Chapter 3.
   Look at the map above. Then explain why Missouri was a slave state, Maine was a free state, and Kansas and Nebraska were given popular sovereignty.

_____

_____

Practice Book

26

Use with *United States: Civil War to Today,* pp. 74–75

Almanac Graph Practice

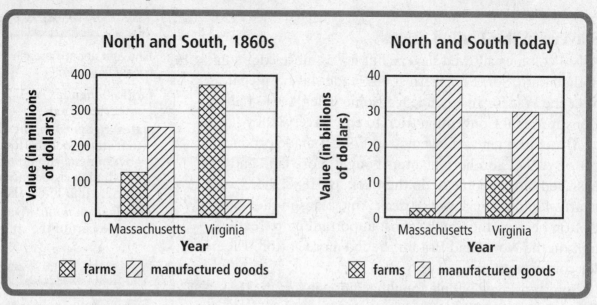

North and South, 1860s

Value (in millions of dollars)

400
300
200
100
0

Massachusetts   Virginia
Year

☒ farms ⬧ manufactured goods

North and South Today

Value (in billions of dollars)

40
30
20
10
0

Massachusetts   Virginia
Year

☒ farms ⬧ manufactured goods

Practice

1. In the 1860s, did southern states such as Virginia rely more on

farming or manufacturing? _____

2. About how many billions of dollars of manufactured goods does

Massachusetts produce today? _____

Apply

3. The information in the chart compares the amount of money people
earned in Massachusetts and Virginia in 1950 and 2000. Use the
data in the chart to complete the double bar graph below.

Personal Income Per Person

State	1950	2000
Massachusetts	1,656	37,960
Virginia	1,257	31,320

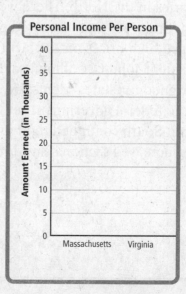

Personal Income Per Person

Amount Earned (in Thousands)

40
35
30
25
20
15
10
5
0

Massachusetts   Virginia

Use with *United States: Civil War to Today*, p. 75

Summary: North and South

Slavery in the United States

All 13 colonies allowed slavery, but it was more common in the South. Some northern states made slavery illegal after the War for Independence. Some delegates to the Constitutional Convention tried to end slavery. They failed.

The cotton gin was invented in 1793. It made producing cotton easier. Southern planters bought more land and enslaved more people to do the work. By 1860, there were nearly 4 million enslaved African Americans in the South. Cotton became the South's most important crop. Textile mills in the North and Britain needed more cotton. The price for cotton went up.

Some enslaved people fought against slavery. In 1831, Nat Turner led a rebellion. New laws were passed to control all African Americans. By the 1850s, they had fewer rights than ever. In the South, many people thought slavery was needed for their economy. In the North, some people thought slavery was wrong.

Economic Differences

In the South, farming was the most important business. Huge plantations had many enslaved workers. Small farms grew food and crops. The North also had farms, but many people moved to cities. They worked in factories, making textiles, shoes, tools, and other things. By 1860, fewer than half of northerners were farmers.

Congress passed tariffs on imported goods. These tariffs helped factories in the North. There were few factories in the South. Prices for manufactured goods were high. People blamed high prices on the tariffs and on the North.

Vice President John C. Calhoun said the tariffs were unfair. He argued for states' rights. He said the Constitution did not let the federal government set tariffs. People in the North and South continued to argue about tariffs and slavery. This increased sectionalism throughout the country.

Before You Read

Find and underline each vocabulary word.

tariff *noun,* a tax on imported goods

states' rights *noun,* the idea that states, not the federal government, should make the final decisions about matters that affect them

sectionalism *noun,* loyalty to one part of the country

After You Read

REVIEW What led to the growth of slavery in the early 1800s? Circle the new invention that changed the South. Then underline the sentence that tells the effect of this invention on slavery in the South. Highlight the sentence that tells what the most important crop in the South was.

REVIEW Why did southerners dislike tariffs? Underline the sentence that tells who the tariffs helped. Circle the sentence that tells what people blamed on the tariffs.

Reading Skill and Strategy

Reading Skill: Compare and Contrast

This skill helps you understand how historical events or people are similar and different.

Read "Economic Differences." Then fill in the chart below to compare and contrast the economics of the North and the South.

North	South
1.	2.

Reading Strategy: Predict/Infer

3. Look over "Slavery in the United States." Then check the best prediction.

   _____ In factories, most workers were enslaved African Americans.

   _____ Most rebellions against slavery were successful in freeing enslaved African Americans.

   _____ Many enslaved African Americans worked in cotton fields in the South.

4. Look over "Economic Differences." Then check the best prediction.

   _____ The northern and southern states agreed that slavery should be abolished.

   _____ Many southerners believed that states had the right to make their own decisions.

   _____ There were more farms in the North than in the South.

Vocabulary and Study Guide

Vocabulary

Write the definition of each vocabulary word below.

1. tariff _____

2. states' rights _____

_____

_____

3. sectionalism _____

4. Use two of the words in a sentence. _____

_____

_____

Study Guide

Read "Slavery in the United States." Then fill in the sequence chart below.

The cotton gin makes cotton much easier to produce.	→	5.	→	Slavery grows rapidly in the South.	→	6.

Read "Economic Differences." Then fill in the compare and contrast chart below.

Region	Economy	Products
South	7.	9.
North	8.	10.

Name _____ Date _____

Skillbuilder: Compare Data Using Graphs

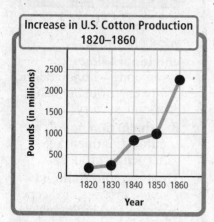

Increase in U.S. Cotton Production 1820–1860

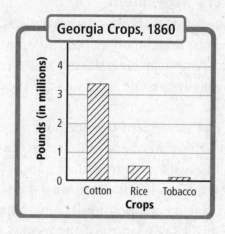

Georgia Crops, 1860

Practice

1. According to the bar graph, what is the difference in pounds between the cotton and tobacco in 1860? _____

2. In what year were 1000 million pounds of cotton produced?

   _____

3. What is the span of years on the line graph? _____

4. How are bar graphs, line graphs, and circle graphs different? _____

   _____

   _____

   _____

Apply

Now use what you know about graphs to redraw the graphs. Draw a bar graph to show that equal amounts of rice and tobacco were produced in 1860. Draw a line graph to show that cotton production decreased steadily from 1800 to 1860. Then draw a circle graph to show that equal amounts of cotton, tobacco, and wheat were exported.

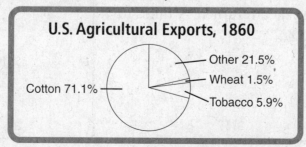

U.S. Agricultural Exports, 1860

Other 21.5%
Wheat 1.5%
Cotton 71.1%
Tobacco 5.9%

Summary: The Fight for Freedom

The Antislavery Movement

Some Americans felt slavery was necessary. In the South, as cotton growing spread, many people also wanted slavery to spread. Other Americans felt slavery was wrong. Some thought that enslaving people went against their religious beliefs.

The abolitionist movement to end slavery grew in the 1830s and 1840s. There were abolitionists in the North and the South. Abolitionists were free blacks and whites, women and men. They wrote and spoke against slavery. William Lloyd Garrison started an abolitionist newspaper called *The Liberator*. Free blacks gave most of the money to support the newspaper.

Frederick Douglass escaped slavery. He spoke to white people about what it was like to be enslaved. Sojourner Truth also escaped slavery. She spoke for abolition and women's rights. Sarah and Angelina Grimké grew up in a Southern slaveowning family. They traveled North and spoke out against slavery.

By 1860, about 500,000 free blacks lived in the United States. They faced discrimination in both the North and South. Free blacks joined whites in creating the American Anti-Slavery Society in 1833.

The Underground Railroad

Some abolitionists worked in secret. Free blacks gave most of the money and did most of the work to support the Underground Railroad. The Underground Railroad was a series of escape routes and hiding places called "stations." Runaways could leave the United States and go north to Canada or south to Mexico, Florida, or the Caribbean. If they were caught, they were returned to slavery and punished. People who guided runaways were called "conductors." The most famous conductor was Harriet Tubman. She escaped slavery and then returned 19 times to the South to lead others to freedom.

Before You Read

Find and underline each vocabulary word.

abolitionist *noun,* someone who joined the movement to abolish, or end, slavery

discrimination *noun,* the unfair treatment of particular groups

Underground Railroad *noun,* a series of escape routes and hiding places to bring slaves out of the South

After You Read

REVIEW **What did free blacks in the North do to convince people that slavery was wrong?** Circle the names of people who took an active part in the abolitionist movement. Underline the actions these people took to help enslaved people. Also underline sentences that tell what all free blacks did to fight slavery.

REVIEW **What was the purpose of the Underground Railroad?** Draw a box around two sentences that explain what the Underground Railroad was and what it was used for.

Reading Skill and Strategy

Reading Skill: Problem and Solution

This skill helps you see what problem some people faced and how they resolved it.

Read "The Fight for Freedom." Then fill in the chart below with solutions for the problem. How did some Americans show their opposition to slavery?

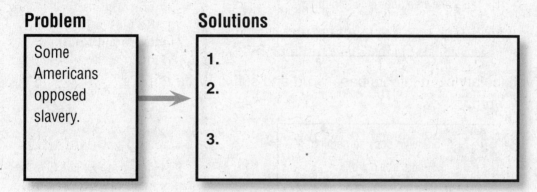

Problem

Some Americans opposed slavery.

Solutions

1.

2.

3.

Reading Strategy: Predict and Infer

4. Look over "The Antislavery Movement." Then check the best prediction.

_____ Many former enslaved African Americans were leading abolitionists.

_____ Most Americans agreed that slavery was good for the nation's economy.

_____ African Americans in the North were treated as equals.

5. Read "The Underground Railroad." Then complete the statement that you can infer.

Many abolitionists believed that Harriet Tubman

_____

Vocabulary and Study Guide

Vocabulary

When you add a suffix to the end of a base word, you make a new word. Knowing a suffix and its base word can help you understand unfamiliar words. Look at the word *conductor*.

> Conduct "to lead or to guide"
> +
> -or "one who does a certain thing"
> =
> Conductor "one who leads or guides"

Break down the vocabulary word into its base word and suffix. Write the meaning of the new word.

> -ist "one who does something"
>
> -tion "the act of"

1. Abolitionist = _____ + _____

   Abolitionist means _____.

2. Discrimination = _____ + _____

   Discrimination means _____.

Study Guide

3. Read "The Antislavery Movement." Then match these people to their identities by drawing a line between the name and the identity.

William Lloyd Garrison	printed antislavery newspaper, *The Liberator*
Frederick Douglass	spoke for abolition and women's rights
Sojourner Truth	spoke to white audiences about slavery

Practice Book
34   Use with *United States: Civil War to Today*, pp. 86–89

Summary: A Nation Divided

Would Slavery Spread?

A territory became a state when it had enough people. New states could be slave states or free states. Northerners wanted free states. They tried to make slavery illegal. Southerners wanted slave states. In 1820, Missouri wanted to enter the Union as a slave state. To keep the number of free and slave states equal, Congress let Maine join as a free state. This was the Missouri Compromise.

Congress drew an imaginary line. Only those states south of the line could be slave states. The Compromise of 1850 let territories choose to be slave states or free states by popular sovereignty. In 1854, Congress gave popular sovereignty to the Kansas and Nebraska territories. Abolitionists objected because both territories were north of the line. Settlers for and against slavery traveled to Kansas to vote. In 1861, Kansas became a free state.

The Growing Crisis

The Fugitive Slave Law was part of the Compromise of 1850. It ordered people to return runaways to slavery. Many northerners would not obey the law. Harriet Beecher Stowe wrote the book *Uncle Tom's Cabin*. It was about the cruelty of slavery. The story convinced northerners to oppose slavery. Southerners said the book was false. The conflict over slavery pushed the North and South further apart.

In 1857, the Supreme Court ruled on the Dred Scott case. It said that slaves were property. Living in a free state did not make them citizens. The Court also said it could not ban slavery in any of the territories. Abolitionists feared slavery would spread.

Abolitionist John Brown thought that slavery was wrong. He tried to start a rebellion against slavery by attacking an Army post in Harpers Ferry, Virginia. Brown was captured, convicted, and hung. Many northerners said he was a hero. By 1860, some southerners wanted to leave the Union to defend their way of life.

Before You Read

Find and underline each vocabulary word.

slave state *noun*, a state that permitted slavery

free state *noun*, a state that did not permit slavery

Union *noun*, another name for the United States

popular sovereignty *noun*, the right of people to make political decisions for themselves

fugitive *noun*, a person who is running away

After You Read

REVIEW **What compromises did Congress make as the nation grew?** Circle the date and name of each compromise.

REVIEW **Why did John Brown attack Harpers Ferry?** Draw a box around the sentence that tells what John Brown thought about slavery.

Reading Skill and Strategy

Reading Skill: Cause and Effect

This skill helps you see how one event can be related to another, either by causing it or resulting from it.

Read "A Nation Divided." Then fill in the chart below to show the effect of the events listed.

Congress had to decide whether to allow slavery in new states.	Dred Scott asked the courts for his freedom.	John Brown led an attack on Harpers Ferry.

1.

Reading Strategy: Predict and Infer

2. Read "Would Slavery Spread?" Then complete the statement that you can infer.

   Some people living in Missouri wanted the right to

   _____.

3. Look over "The Growing Crisis." Read the headings. Make a prediction about what the section will be about.

   _____

   _____

4. Read "Would Slavery Spread?" Why did Kansas join the Union as a free state?

   _____

   _____

Name _____ Date _____

Vocabulary and Study Guide

Vocabulary

1. Draw a line connecting the vocabulary word to its meaning.

Union	did not permit slavery
fugitive	when people who live in a place make the decisions
free state	a person who is running away
slave state	permitted slavery
popular sovereignty	another name for the United States

Study Guide

Read "Would Slavery Spread?" Then fill in the main idea and details chart below.

Compromise	What it did
Missouri Compromise	**2.**
Compromise of 1850	**3.**
Kansas-Nebraska Act	**4.**

Read "The Growing Crisis." Then answer the question.

5. What are three events that increased tension between the North and South?

_____

_____

Summary: Civil War Begins

Abraham Lincoln

Conflict grew between the North and South. Southerners thought abolitionists would start slave rebellions. Some southerners wanted to leave the Union. Northerners were afraid slavery would spread. Americans who opposed slavery formed the Republican Party. Republicans opposed slavery in the territories.

Abraham Lincoln was a Republican. He was born in Kentucky, a slave state. He was raised on a farm in Illinois, a free state. His family was poor. He did not go to school, but he read a lot. Lincoln became a lawyer and a political leader.

Lincoln's Campaigns

In 1858, Lincoln ran for Senate in Illinois against Stephen Douglas. They debated so people could hear their ideas. Douglas wanted popular sovereignty for territories. He did not think slavery was wrong. Lincoln said slavery was evil, but he did not support abolition. Lincoln lost, but the debates made him famous. Many southerners thought he wanted to abolish slavery.

Lincoln ran for president in 1860. He was the only candidate against slavery. He won, but the election showed that the country was divided. No southern states voted for Lincoln. Some southerners said the federal government was too strong. They said tariffs and laws to limit slavery threatened states' rights. Some chose secession to protect their right to enslave people.

Secession Begins

In 1860, South Carolina left the union. In all, 11 southern states formed the Confederacy. Jefferson Davis was president. Lincoln wanted unity and peace but it was too late. Confederates attacked Fort Sumter on April 12, 1861. Lincoln called for men to fight the rebellion. The Civil War began.

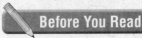

Before You Read

Find and underline each vocabulary word.

secession *noun*, when part of a country leaves or breaks off from the rest

Confederate States of America *noun*, the name chosen by the states that left the Union at the time of the Civil War

Civil War *noun*, the war between the North and the South

After You Read

REVIEW **Why did some southerners want their states to secede?** Draw a box around three sentences that tell what southerners said about the federal government, what they thought threatened states' rights, and what right they wanted to protect.

REVIEW **Why did southerners see Lincoln as an enemy?** Circle what Lincoln said about slavery. Also circle what southerners thought he would do about slavery.

REVIEW **What event began the Civil War?** What happened on April 12, 1861? Draw a box around the answer.

Practice Book
38
Use with *United States: Civil War to Today*, pp. 102–107

Reading Skill and Strategy

Reading Skill: Sequence

This skill helps you understand the order in which events happened.

Read "Civil War Begins." Then fill in the sequence chart below to show the order in which Abraham Lincoln became President.

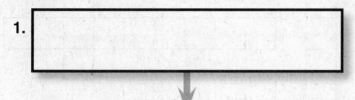

1.

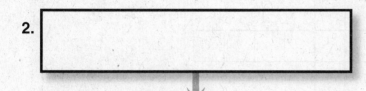

2.

Lincoln was elected even though he did not win any southern states.

Reading Strategy: Predict and Infer

3. Read "Abraham Lincoln" and "Lincoln's Campaigns." Use the information in these sections to make a prediction about what you will learn in the final section, "Secession Begins."

_____

_____

_____

4. Read "Secession Begins." Predict what will happen in the next chapter.

_____

_____

_____

39   Use with *United States: Civil War to Today*, pp. 102–107

Vocabulary and Study Guide

Vocabulary

Across

1. Seven southern states left the Union and formed the Confederate States of America, or the _____.
2. What southerners called for to protect their right to own enslaved people
3. Said to the South, "We are not enemies, but friends"
4. An issue dividing the North and South

Down

1. Began with the attack on Fort Sumter
5. President of the Confederate States

Study Guide

6. Read "Abraham Lincoln" and "Lincoln's Campaigns." Then fill in the blanks below.

Abraham Lincoln was born in _____, but his family moved to _____ when he was a boy. Lincoln studied and became a successful _____. He was a member of the _____ Party. He also became a member of the Illinois legislature and later served one term in the _____.

Lincoln argued against the spread of slavery, but he did not call for _____.

7. Read "Secession Begins." Then fill in the blanks below.

Seven southern states decided to leave the Union and form the _____ States of America. The South Carolina state militia surrounded _____, which had U.S. soldiers inside. When President Lincoln sent _____ to the fort, the Confederacy fired on the fort with cannons. This was the start of the _____.

Summary: The States at War

North Against South

Eleven southern states left the Union and formed the Confederacy. Four border states stayed in the Union. The North wanted to keep the Union together. They planned to stop the Confederacy from trading with other nations. They would attack the South from the East and West at the same time. The North had more people, factories, and railroads. The South planned to fight off northern attacks until the Confederacy could survive as a nation. The South had good military leaders. They hoped France and Britain would help because these countries needed southern cotton. Most of the war was in the South, so Confederate soldiers knew the land. Both sides thought they could win quickly. In July 1861, at the Battle of Bull Run they learned the war might last a long time.

The War's Leaders

Robert E. Lee led the Confederate army. He stopped the Union army from capturing Richmond, Virginia. He invaded the North. The Union army stopped him at Antietam in September 1862. There were 23,000 casualties in one day. Union General Ulysses S. Grant captured Confederate forts in the West and defeated the Confederates at Shiloh. Because the ports were blocked, the South was low on food, weapons, and money. The Confederacy had to draft soldiers. In the North, rich people could pay to get out of the draft. People who were too poor to pay protested. So did people who opposed the whole war.

Turning Points

In 1863, Lincoln made the Emancipation Proclamation, freeing the enslaved people. The Union captured Vicksburg, Mississippi and won control of the Mississippi River. Lee attacked the North, and the Union beat him at Gettysburg, Pennsylvania.

Before You Read

Find and underline each vocabulary word.

border states *noun*, slave states that stayed in the Union

casualties *noun*, soldiers who are killed or wounded

draft *noun*, government selection of people to serve in the military

emancipation *noun*, the freeing of enslaved people

After You Read

REVIEW **What was the Confederacy's plan for winning the war?** Highlight the sentence that tells what the South planned to do.

REVIEW **Why did people in the North oppose the draft?** Underline the sentences that tell you the answer.

REVIEW **Why was the victory at Vicksburg important to the Union?** Circle the sentence that tells you the answer.

Practice Book
41
Use with *United States: Civil War to Today*, pp. 114–119

Reading Skill and Strategy

Reading Skill: Classify

This skill helps you understand and remember what you have read by organizing facts into groups, or categories.

Read "North Against South." What were the advantages for the Union and the Confederacy?

Union	Confederacy
1. _____ _____	2. _____ _____
3. _____	4. _____

Reading Strategy: Summarize

5. Read "North Against South." Then check the best summary.

____ The North and the South had different advantages in the war.

____ There were more people in the North than in the South.

____ The Confederacy defeated the Union at the First Battle of Bull Run.

6. Read "The War's Leaders." Then check the best summary.

____ The Union had many more generals than the Confederacy.

____ General Lee and General Grant fought each other in many battles.

____ Political and military leaders were very important during the Civil War.

Use with *United States: Civil War to Today*, pp. 114–119

Vocabulary and Study Guide

Vocabulary

Write the word for each definition below.

1. Slave states that stayed in the Union when the Civil War began

   _____

2. Soldiers who are killed or wounded _____

3. When the government selects people to be soldiers _____

4. The freeing of enslaved people _____

Study Guide

Read "North Against South." Then fill in the comparison chart below.

	Advantages	Strategies
Union	Larger population; More factories and railroad lines	5.
Confederacy	6.	7.

8. Read "The War's Leaders" and "Turning Points." Then fill in the blanks below.

   At the start of the Civil War, President Lincoln did not plan

   to _____ enslaved people. Then

   Lincoln made the _____ to weaken

   the Confederacy. After that, the Civil War became a war to end

   _____. In 1863, the Union won an impor-

   tant battle at _____ and gained

   full control of the Mississippi River. The Union also won the Battle

   of Gettysburg, where President Lincoln later made a famous speech

   called the _____.

Practice Book
43   Use with *United States: Civil War to Today*, pp. 114–119

Summary: Life in Battle, Life at Home

The Soldier's Life

Men from all over the country fought in the Civil War. Many soldiers hoped for excitement but found terror on the battlefield. Life in the camp was hard. Soldiers lived in tents. The food was not good. Confederate soldiers didn't have enough food. Many soldiers were killed by new rifles. However, twice as many died from diseases. At first almost all the soldiers were white men. About 180,000 African Americans served in the Union army. Immigrants from Ireland, Germany, and Italy also fought for the Union. American Indians fought on both sides. Thousands of boys went into battle even though they were too young. Some boys were drummers who sent signals during battles. Women on both sides disguised themselves as men and joined the army. Women also worked as spies. More than 3,000 women in the North and many women in the South nursed the sick and wounded. One nurse, Clara Barton, later founded the Red Cross.

On the Home Front

Soldiers left their families to go to war. The families made up the home front. With men gone, women took on new tasks. They ran farms and businesses. They sewed uniforms, knitted socks, made bandages, and raised money. Most of the battles were in the South. Civilians in the North could not see the war happening. Matthew Brady used the new technology of photography to show them. He took pictures of soldiers in camp and on the battlefield. People in the South saw their cities, homes, and barns destroyed in the war. Inflation, or a rise in prices, made food very expensive. Soldiers and civilians in the South often did not have enough to eat. Enslaved people also suffered, but they thought the war would bring freedom. The Emancipation Proclamation in 1863 gave them hope. News of emancipation did not get to Texas until June 19, 1865. That day is celebrated as Juneteenth, the day slavery ended, in many parts of the South.

Before You Read

Find and underline each vocabulary word.

camp *noun,* a group of temporary shelters, such as tents

home front *noun,* all the people who are not in the military when a country is at war

civilian *noun,* a person who is not in the military

After You Read

REVIEW **What did women on both sides of the war do to help their side?** Draw a box around the sentences that tell how women helped in the Civil War.

REVIEW **What happened to prices in the South during the Civil War?** Underline the sentence that tells how the price of food changed during the Civil War. Then highlight the effect of higher prices for civilians and soldiers.

Reading Skill and Strategy

Reading Skill: Main Idea and Details

This skill helps you understand events by seeing how they are related.

Read "The Soldier's Life" and "On the Home Front." Then fill in the webs below. Write details that support each main idea in the smaller ovals. You can add more small ovals if you need them.

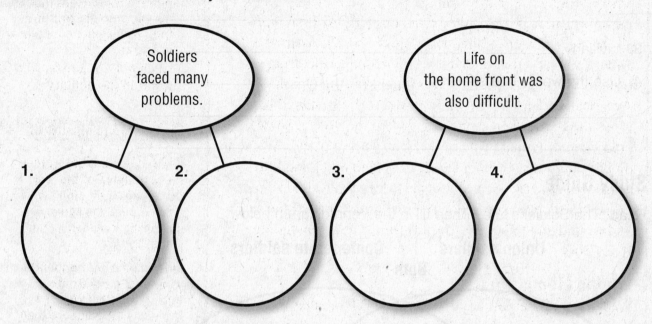

Reading Strategy: Summarize

5. Read "The Soldier's Life." Then check the best summary.

   ____ Fighting battles was only one of the problems soldiers faced.

   ____ Soldiers in the Union army made lots of money during the war.

   ____ Most Confederate soldiers died during the many battles with the Union.

6. Read "On the Home Front." Then complete the summary.

   During the Civil War, life was very hard for civilians, especially

   for _____.

Name _____ Date _____

Vocabulary and Study Guide

Vocabulary

Write the definition of each vocabulary word below.

1. camp _____

2. home front _____

   _____

3. civilian _____

4. Use the words in a sentence. _____

   _____

   _____

Study Guide

Read "The Soldier's Life." Then fill in the Venn diagram below.

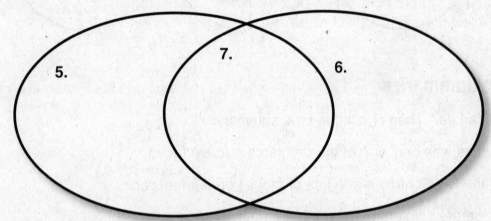

Read "On the Home Front." Then answer the questions.

8. Why did people in the North need photographs to understand camp life and battles?

   _____

9. Why was life especially hard in the South during the war?

   _____

   _____

Summary: The Union Advances

Union Victories

After winning the battles of Vicksburg and Gettysburg in 1863, the North hoped they would win the war. The South kept fighting. Lincoln needed a tough army general to defeat the South. He chose Ulysses S. Grant. Grant sent General William Tecumseh Sherman to lead the Union army in Tennessee. In September 1864, Sherman captured Atlanta, Georgia, and sent Lincoln a message by telegraph, telling of his victory. The Union navy also captured Mobile Bay in Alabama. Lincoln needed victories to win voters' support for reelection. Sherman's army marched from Atlanta to the coast and into South Carolina. He ordered his troops to use total war so the southerners would give up. His soldiers destroyed any resources the Confederacy could use to fight. They stole food and killed livestock. They wrecked factories and railroad lines. They burned homes and barns.

Grant and Lee

While Sherman marched through Georgia and South Carolina in 1864, General Grant led a huge army toward Richmond, Virginia. They were opposed by Robert E. Lee and his army. The Union army suffered many casualties, but Grant kept attacking. Lee was forced to retreat farther south. In June 1864, the two armies faced each other near Richmond. They fought for almost a year. The Union army was getting stronger. They had plenty of supplies and soldiers. Lee's army was getting weaker. The Confederacy had no more money for supplies. They had no more soldiers to send to the front. The soldiers were hungry and tired. Some decided to desert. In April 1865, Grant captured Richmond. Grant's soldiers chased Lee's army west. Lee's army was starving and almost surrounded. On April 9, 1865 Lee surrendered to Grant at Appomattox Court House. The Union soldiers saluted their enemies as they marched past. The war was finally over.

Before You Read

Find and underline each vocabulary word.

telegraph *noun*, a machine that sends electric signals over wires

total war *noun*, the strategy of destroying an enemy's resources

desert *verb*, to leave the army without permission

After You Read

REVIEW Why did Sherman decide to use total war against the South? Highlight the sentence that tells you the answer.

REVIEW Why did Lee have to surrender? Underline the sentences that tell about Lee's army while fighting in Richmond and after the Union soldiers captured Richmond. Circle the sentences that tell about the Confederacy's supplies and soldiers.

Use with *United States: Civil War to Today*, pp. 128–131

Reading Skill and Strategy

Reading Skill: Predict Outcomes

This skill allows you to think about what might happen, based on what you have read.

Read the first paragraph of "Grant and Lee." Then fill in the prediction chart below. Write what you think happened with Lee in charge of the army in the first box. Then read the next paragraph. Write what happened with Lee in charge in the second box.

1. | **Prediction:**

2. | **Outcome:**

Reading Strategy: Summarize

3. Read "Union Victories." Then complete the summary.

   The Union army destroyed land in the South to force

   _____.

4. Read "Grant and Lee." Then write a short summary of the section.

   _____

   _____

   _____

Vocabulary and Study Guide

Vocabulary

Write the definition of each vocabulary word below.

1. telegraph _____

_____

2. total war _____

_____

3. desert _____

Study Guide

Read "Union Victories." Then answer the questions.

4. What two Union victories further weakened the Confederacy?

_____

_____

5. Why did General Sherman want to use total war on the South?

_____

_____

Read "Grant and Lee." Then fill in the causes-and-effect chart below.

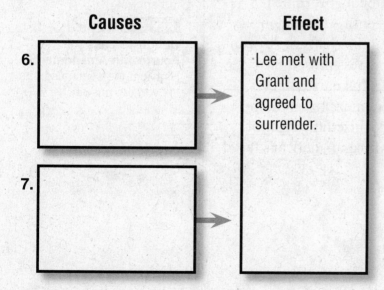

Causes   **Effect**

6. [ ] → Lee met with Grant and agreed to surrender.

7. [ ]

Use with *United States: Civil War to Today*, pp. 128–131

Summary: Rebuilding a Nation

Various Plans for Reconstruction

After the war, the country had to be reunited. This period was called Reconstruction. Some northerners wanted to punish the South. Lincoln asked people to forget their anger. He wanted the defeated states to set up state governments and rejoin the Union quickly. Radical Republicans in Congress wanted to change the South and protect the rights of African Americans. Lincoln was shot on April 14, 1865 by John Wilkes Booth. His assassination shocked the country.

Reconstruction

Vice President Andrew Johnson became president. He put Lincoln's plan into action. Southern states had to abolish slavery. Most passed Black Codes to limit the rights of African Americans. Congress set up the Freedmen's Bureau to provide support for poor blacks and whites. In 1867, Congress put the South under military rule. Soldiers forced states to obey Congress and pass laws letting all men vote. In 1868, Congress impeached Johnson. They said he broke laws. Some southerners supported Congress. They were called scalawags. Some northerners went to the South just to make money. They were called carpetbaggers.

The Constitution Changes

During Reconstruction, Congress created three amendments to the Constitution. They gave the national government more power over the states. The Thirteenth Amendment ended slavery. Black Codes still limited the rights of African Americans. To protect those rights Congress passed the Fourteenth Amendment. It gave blacks full citizenship. Southern states had to ratify this amendment to rejoin the Union. The Fifteenth Amendment recognized the right of African American men to vote. But African Americans faced a long struggle for equality.

Before You Read

Find and underline each vocabulary word.

Reconstruction *noun*, the period when the South rejoined the Union

assassination *noun*, the murder of an important leader

Freedmen's Bureau *noun*, an agency set up to provide food, clothing, medical care, and legal advice to poor blacks and whites

impeach *verb*, to charge a government official with a crime

After You Read

REVIEW What was Lincoln's plan for reconstruction? Underline the sentence that tells you the answer.

REVIEW Why were soldiers sent to the South? Circle the sentence that tells the answer.

REVIEW Why did Congress pass the Fourteenth Amendment? Highlight the sentences that tell you the answer.

Reading Skill and Strategy

Reading Skill: Draw Conclusions

Sometimes when you read, you have to figure out things that the writer doesn't tell you. This skill is called drawing conclusions.

Read "Various Plans for Reconstruction." Then fill in the draw conclusions chart below. What conclusion can you draw from the different groups' plans to rebuild the South?

Some people wanted to make it easy for the South to come back into the Union.	Some people wanted to punish the South.	Some people wanted to protect the rights of African Americans.

1. _____

Reading Strategy: Summarize

2. Read "Reconstruction." Then complete the summary.

   _____ in Congress disagreed with how

   President Johnson let the South rebuild itself.

3. Read "The Constitution Changes." Then write a sentence to summarize the section.

   _____

   _____

   _____

51   Use with *United States: Civil War to Today*, pp. 136–141

Vocabulary and Study Guide

Vocabulary

1. Draw a line connecting the vocabulary word to its meaning.

Reconstruction	To charge a government official with a crime
assassination	The agency that provided food, clothing, medical care, and legal advice to poor blacks and whites
Freedmen's Bureau	Murder of an important leader
impeach	The period when the South rejoined the Union

Study Guide

2. Read "Reconstruction." Then fill in the blanks below.

After President Lincoln was _____,

_____ became President. Radical Republicans

became upset because of the South's _____

and because the new President allowed the election of former

_____ leaders to Congress. Congress fought

back by passing a law to protect the _____

of freedmen and creating the _____.

3. Read "The Constitution Changes." Then fill in the blanks below.

Congress created the Thirteenth, Fourteenth, and Fifteenth

_____ to protect the rights of _____.

These amendments gave the national government more power over

_____. African Americans were granted full

_____ and the right to fair and equal treatment.

Some African American men became government leaders.

Skillbuilder: Compare Primary and Secondary Sources

"A house divided against itself cannot stand. I believe this government cannot endure, permanently half slave and half free. I do not expect the Union to be dissolved—I do not expect the house to fall—but I do expect it will cease to be divided. It will become all one thing or all the other."

—Abraham Lincoln, in an 1858 campaign speech to Illinois Republicans

Lincoln Becomes a Leading Antislavery Spokesperson

Americans began to learn of Abraham Lincoln's views on slavery when he challenged Stephen Douglas in the 1858 Illinois Senate election. Lincoln did not speak to outlaw slavery in the South, but he did not think the country could continue to be half slave states and half free states. He believed that soon the country would have to become all slave or all free states.

Practice

1. Is Abraham Lincoln's speech a primary or secondary source? How do you know? _____

2. What facts do the two sources share? _____

_____

_____

3. What do you learn from the passage that you do not learn from Lincoln's speech? _____

_____

Apply

Find a book that is an example of a primary source. Then find a book that is an example of a secondary source. On a separate sheet of paper, write a paragraph explaining how you identified each one.

53   Use with *United States: Civil War to Today*, pp. 144–145

Summary: Freedom and Hardship

Freedom and Hardship

Reconstruction was a time of hope for African Americans. Slavery was over. New laws protected their rights. The plantation system was over. African Americans knew how to farm, but they could not afford to buy land. Some landowners let freed African Americans farm on their land. This system was called sharecropping. Landowners loaned sharecroppers tools and seeds. Sharecroppers gave the landowners a share of the crop. Often sharecroppers did not make enough money to pay their debts.

Some southerners opposed Reconstruction. They did not like federal troops in their states. They did not support laws that gave rights to African Americans. People formed secret organizations, like the Ku Klux Klan, to stop African Americans from taking part in government. They threatened, beat, and killed African Americans to stop them from voting.

The End of Reconstruction

By 1877 many people thought Reconstruction had not reunited the nation. President Rutherford B. Hayes told the federal troops to leave the South. Without soldiers to protect them, many African Americans could not vote. They lost their political power. Southern states passed Jim Crow laws to keep African Americans separate. Segregation was enforced in schools, hospitals, even cemeteries. The states usually spent less money on schools and hospitals for African Americans. Many African Americans believed education was important. In 1881, a former slave named Booker T. Washington opened the Tuskegee Institute where students studied and learned useful skills. The teachers and students were African Americans. Washington believed that educated African Americans would get equal treatment. Churches became important centers in African American communities.

Before You Read

Find and underline each vocabulary word.

sharecropping *noun*, system where farmers used land and gave landowners a share of the crop

Jim Crow *noun*, laws that kept African Americans separate from other Americans

segregation *noun*, the forced separation of the races

After You Read

REVIEW **Why did many freed African Americans become sharecroppers?** Underline the sentence that tells the answer.

REVIEW **What was the purpose of the Tuskegee Institute?** Circle the name of the man who started the Tuskegee Institute. Then highlight the words that tell what people did at the Institute.

Reading Skill and Strategy

Reading Skill: Problem and Solution

This skill helps you see what problem some people faced and how they resolved it.

Read "Freedom and Hardship." Then fill in the problem-and-solution chart below. What happened to the freed people during and after Reconstruction?

Problems	Solutions
1.	Many African Americans became sharecroppers.
Government soldiers left the South.	2.

Reading Strategy: Summarize

3. Read "Freedom and Hardship." Then write a short summary of each section.

Section 1: Freedom and Hardship

Summary: _____

_____

Section 2: The End of Reconstruction

Summary: _____

_____

_____

55   Use with *United States: Civil War to Today*, pp. 146–149

Vocabulary and Study Guide

Vocabulary

Write the definition of each vocabulary word below.

1. sharecropping _____

_____

_____

2. Jim Crow _____

_____

3. segregation _____

4. Use two of the words in a sentence.

_____

_____

_____

Study Guide

Read "Freedom and Hardship." Then fill in the causes-and-effects chart below.

Causes		Effects
Many African Americans became sharecroppers.	→	**5.**
6.	→	They formed the Ku Klux Klan.

Practice Book
56 Use with *United States: Civil War to Today*, pp. 146–149

Name _____ Date _____

Almanac Map Practice

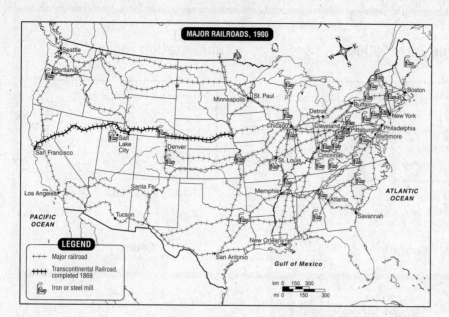

MAJOR RAILROADS, 1900

LEGEND
+++ Major railroad
+++ Transcontinental Railroad, completed 1869
Iron or steel mill.

Use the map to do these activities and answer these questions.

Practice

1. Draw a line along the route of the transcontinental railroad.

2. In what city did the transcontinental railroad end?

   _____

3. Where were most steel mills located? _____

4. Circle a symbol that shows an iron mill.

Apply

5. With a partner, plan a trip on a U.S. railroad route of the 1900s. Choose a starting point in your state. Then choose an end point somewhere else in the United States. Figure out which railroads you would have to take to make your journey. Trace your journey on the map. List the cities through which you would pass.

   _____

   _____

Use with *United States: Civil War to Today*, pp. 158–159

Name _____ Date _____ UNIT 3

Almanac Graph Practice

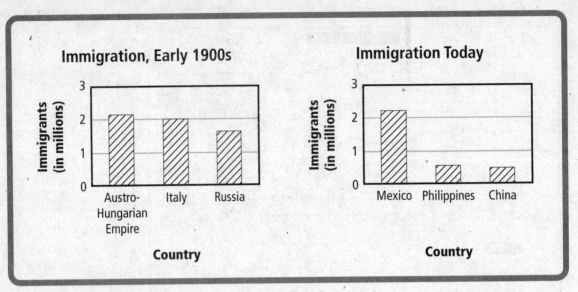

Immigration, Early 1900s

Immigration Today

Use the above graphs to answer these questions.

Practice

1. About how many people moved to the United States from Italy in the
   early 1900s? _____

2. Have more people immigrated to the United States from Mexico or
   from China? _____

Apply

3. Complete the bar graph using the data in the chart below.

United States Immigration

Time Period	Number
1901–1910	8,795,000
1941–1950	1,035,000
1991–2000	9,095,000

United States Immigration

Use with *United States: Civil War to Today,* p. 159

Summary: Connecting the Country

The Telegraph Helps Communication

In the early 1800s, letters and news traveled by horse, stagecoach, or steamboat. Sometimes news from one part of the country didn't reach another part for several weeks. In 1844, a new kind of communication was introduced. The new telegraph machine sent electric signals through wires to a distant location. Samuel Morse invented a code for sending messages. People could send and get messages in just a few minutes. By 1861, telegraph wires stretched from coast to coast. Reporters sent news stories to their newspapers, and people sent personal messages and business information. During the Civil War, battle plans were made using the telegraph.

A Transcontinental Railroad

Many Americans began moving west by the 1840s. They were looking for gold or for new places to settle. There were only two good ways to travel. One way was to sail around the tip of South America. The other way was to travel to the end of the railroad line and take a rough trail on land in wagons pulled by horses, mule, or oxen. Both ways were long, difficult, and expensive. In 1862, railroad companies got money and land from Congress to build a transcontinental railroad to connect the coasts. The Union Pacific hired former Civil War soldiers, formerly enslaved African Americans, and Irish immigrants to build track from east to west. They started in Nebraska with existing railroad lines from the East Coast. The Central Pacific hired many Chinese immigrants to lay tracks from west to east, starting in California. Because of prejudice, these workers were paid less than other workers and given the most dangerous jobs.

The two tracks met at Promontory Point, Utah, on May 10, 1869, to make a 1,800-mile-long transcontinental railroad. It was the first of several railroads. It was easier to cross the continent by train. Western farmers made money by shipping cattle and wheat to the East.

Before You Read

Find and underline each vocabulary word.

transcontinental *adjective*, crossing a continent

prejudice *noun*, an unfair negative opinion that can lead to unjust treatment

After You Read

REVIEW How did people travel west in the 1840s? Circle the two sentences that tell how people traveled.

REVIEW What kinds of goods were shipped on transcontinental railroads? Circle the words that describe what western farmers sold to the East in order to make money.

Reading Skill and Strategy

Reading Skill: Predict Outcome

This skill allows you to think about what might happen, based on what you have read.

Read the first two paragraphs of "The Telegraph Helps Communication." In the top box, write what you think happened to the way people communicated after the telegraph was invented. Then read the last two paragraphs of the section. In the bottom box, write how the telegraph improved communication for people.

Prediction

1. [   ]

Outcome

2. [   ]

Reading Strategy: Monitor/Clarify

3. Read "The Telegraph Helps Communication." Then check the statement that best clarifies the section.

____ Messages could be sent more quickly using the telegraph.

____ After the invention of the telegraph, people stopped writing letters.

____ It took only three minutes to send a telegraph message from Chicago to Boston.

4. Read "A Transcontinental Railroad." Then check the statement that best clarifies the section.

____ Workers built the railroad to connect the United States and Canada.

____ Traveling from the East to the West in a wagon was slow and expensive.

____ The transcontinental railroad allowed southern farmers to ship goods to the North.

Use with *United States: Civil War to Today*, pp. 162–165

Vocabulary and Study Guide

Vocabulary

Write the definition of each vocabulary word below.

1. transcontinental _____

2. prejudice _____

Use each word in a sentence about the lesson.

3. _____

_____

4. _____

_____

_____

Study Guide

5. Read "The Telegraph Helps Communication." Then fill in the blanks below.

_____ invented the telegraph in 1844.

The telegraph used _____ over wires

to send messages very _____ over long

distances. Companies built telegraph lines that could carry

_____ from the East Coast to the West Coast.

The _____ helped bankers, war generals, and

reporters do their jobs better.

Read "The Effects of the Railroads." Then fill in the effects in the chart below.

Cause		Effects
The transcontinental railroad was completed in 1869.	**6.** →	
	7. →	

Skillbuilder: Read a Time Zone Map

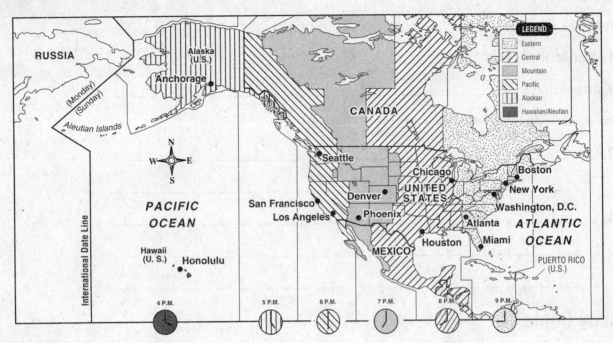

Practice

1. In what time zone is Seattle, Washington? _____

2. On the map, circle the U.S. city that is nearest to the International

Date Line.

3. As you go east from Chicago to Boston, do you add or subtract

one hour? _____

4. In what time zone do you live? _____

_____

Apply

Use your map skills to add more information to this map. Look at the
region that is east of the Eastern Time Zone. Label it Atlantic Standard
Time on the map and on the legend. Use a color or pattern to show that
the Atlantic Standard Time Zone is different from the other six time zones.

Practice Book
62   Use with *United States: Civil War to Today*, pp. 168–169

Summary: Moving to the Plains

Settling the Great Plains

In the early 1800s, few people lived on the Great Plains. The Great Plains are in the middle of the United States. People did not think the land was good for farming. It was very dry and flat.

In 1862, the Homestead Act was passed. The government helped people to settle on the Great Plains. The government sold adults 160 acres of land for a small amount of money. If they could farm the land for five years, they could own it. A settler's home and land was called a homestead. Many homesteaders came from the eastern United States, where farmland cost a lot. In the Great Plains, land was cheaper. Settlers also came from Europe, where there was not much land to buy. There was a lot of land to buy in the Great Plains. African Americans also wanted to start farms. Many African Americans were poor. They faced prejudice and violence after the Civil War. They started their own towns in Kansas. African American settlers were called Exodusters, after a book in the Bible that tells the story of how people escaped slavery.

Settlers Face Hardships

Settlers had to learn how to farm on the Great Plains. The soil was held together by grass roots. It was called sod. Settlers were called sodbusters because they had to break through the sod to plant crops. There was not a lot of wood, so settlers used sod to build homes. Winters were long and cold. Summers were hot and dry. There were many droughts. There were grass fires because it was so dry. Farmers had to grow crops that did not need much water. They carried water from streams. Some farmers used windmills to pump water from underground. In the 1870s, millions of grasshoppers ate the crops. There weren't many people in the area to do farm work, so farmers used new and better farm machines. New machines made it faster and easier to grow more crops.

Before You Read

Find and underline each vocabulary word.

homestead *noun*, a settler's home and land

Exodusters *noun*, African American settlers who moved to the Great Plains

drought *noun*, a long period with little or no rain

sodbuster *noun*, name given to a settler who had to break through sod to build houses and plant crops

After You Read

REVIEW **Why did settlers from Europe and the East move to the Great Plains?** Circle two reasons why these settlers moved.

REVIEW **Why was life on the Great Plains so difficult?** Underline sentences that describe the land.

REVIEW **How did settlers adapt to the lack of extra workers on the Great Plains?** Underline what the settlers did to make growing crops easier and faster.

Reading Skill and Strategy

Reading Skill: Problem and Solution

This skill helps you see what problems some people faced and how they resolved them.

Read "Settlers Face Hardships." How did the settlers overcome the problems of living on and farming the Great Plains?

Problems	Solutions
Settlers wanted to build houses.	1. _____
Farmers had to find more water for their crops.	2. _____ _____
Farmers needed help on their farms to get the work done.	3. _____ _____

Reading Strategy: Monitor/Clarify

4. Read "Settling the Great Plains." Then check the statement that best clarifies the section.

_____ Farmers moved away from the Great Plains in search of better farmland.

_____ People from Europe avoided farming on the Great Plains.

_____ The Exodusters were African American farmers who moved to Kansas in the late 1800s.

5. Read "Settlers Face Hardships." Then complete the following statement about the settlers' homes.

The main advantage of using sod was that the homes stayed

_____.

Use with *United States: Civil War to Today*, pp. 170–175

Vocabulary and Study Guide

Vocabulary

1. Draw a line connecting the vocabulary word to its meaning.

sodbuster	a settler's house and land
homestead	a long period without rain
Exodusters	the name for a Great Plains farmer
drought	African American settlers who moved from the South to the Great Plains

Study Guide

2. Read "Settling the Great Plains." Name three groups of people who settled on the Great Plains after Congress passed the Homestead Act.

_____

_____

_____

3. Read "Settlers Face Hardships." Then fill in the blanks below.

Settlers found ways to adapt to the harsh _____

of the Great Plains. Trees were scarce so the settlers used sod

to _____. They also used new and improved

_____ to take the place of extra workers. Wheat

seeds from the East did not grow well in a climate with so little

_____, so Great Plains settlers tried wheat seeds

from _____, which grew very well.

Practice Book
65 Use with *United States: Civil War to Today*, pp. 170–175

Summary: Cattle Drivers

Texas Cattle

In the 1860s, millions of longhorn cattle lived in Texas. They were strong animals that were first brought to North America by Spanish settlers. They ate grass and did not need a lot of water. Cowhands made sure the cows did not run away. They herded the cattle.

Cattle ranchers could not make much money selling their cattle in Texas because there were so few people. There was a big supply of cattle, but not a big demand. So the price of cattle was low. In the eastern and northern parts of the United States, people wanted to buy cattle products. So cattle prices were high.

The Cattle Drives

The cattle ranchers wanted to sell their cattle in the East and North. They could get better prices because the demand was high and the supply was low. Cattle ranchers needed to get their cattle to railroads that were often hundreds of miles from the cattle ranches. Ranchers hired cowhands to take their cattle on cattle drives to the railheads. In a cattle drive, cowhands rode on horseback next to the herd of cattle to make them move. They stayed near rivers so that the cattle had water to drink. The work was dirty, hard, and dangerous.

The cattle drives ended in the late 1880s for several reasons. First, there was the invention of barbed wire. This wire had sharp points on it. Settlers used barbed wire to make fences on their property. The fences blocked the cattle trails. Second, more railroads were built. Railheads were closer to the ranches. Third, too many cattle grazed on crowded ranges, and there was not enough grass to feed all the cattle. Finally, the terrible winter of 1886–1887 killed thousands of cattle.

 Before You Read

Find and underline each vocabulary word.

supply *noun*, the amount of something that people want to sell at certain prices

demand *noun*, the amount of something that people want to buy at certain prices

railhead *noun*, a town where railroad tracks begin or end

barbed wire *noun*, twisted wire with a sharp barb, or point, every few inches

After You Read

REVIEW **Why did Texas cattle ranchers want to sell their animals in the East and North?** Highlight the sentence that answers the question.

REVIEW **Why did big cattle drives end?** Circle the reasons why cattle drives ended.

Use with *United States: Civil War to Today*, pp. 178–181

Reading Skill and Strategy

Reading Skill: Cause and Effect

This skill helps you see how one event can be related to another, either by causing it or resulting from it.

Read "The Cattle Drives." What two effects were caused by the demand for cattle products in the North and the East?

Cause	Effects
High demand for cattle products in the North and the East	1. 2.

Reading Strategy: Monitor/Clarify

3. Read "Demand and Supply for Cattle" Then read the explanation of *demand* and explain what *supply* is.

   Demand is how much of something people will buy at a set price.

   Supply is _____

   _____.

4. Read "The End of the Drives." Explain what you know about barbed

   wire. _____

   _____

   _____

67   Use with *United States: Civil War to Today*, pp. 178–181

Vocabulary and Study Guide

Vocabulary

demand	railhead	barbed wire	supply

1. Write two vocabulary words under each heading.

Affected cattle drives	Affected cattle prices

2. Choose two words. Use each word in a sentence about the lesson.

_____

_____

_____

Study Guide

Read "Texas Cattle." Then choose the correct ending to each statement below.

3. Longhorn cattle were originally brought to Texas by

    A. cowhands.   **B.** vaqueros.   **C.** Spanish settlers.

4. In Texas, the abundance of cattle created a

    A. high demand.   **B.** low demand.   **C.** unstable demand.

5. In the East and North, the low supply of cattle made prices

    A. high.   **B.** low.   **C.** change often.

6. Read "The Cattle Drives." Then fill in the blanks below.

    The cattle drives only lasted for about _____. Fences

made of _____ put up by new settlers on their land blocked

the cattle trails. When the _____ grew, ranchers no longer

had to drive their cattle hundreds of miles to reach a _____.

Use with *United States: Civil War to Today*, pp. 178–181

Name _____ Date _____

Summary: War on the Plains

War on the Plains

In the 1840s, settlers moved west to the Great Plains. They were looking for land or gold. The government built roads and railroads for the settlers. Many Indians lived on the Great Plains. The government tried to get them to sell their land. The government wanted the Indians to move to reservations.

The Plains Indians did not want to live and farm on the reservations. The reservations were small. The land was poor. Most of the Indians were not farmers. They were hunters. For years, millions of buffalo lived on the Great Plains. The Indians hunted them to get food and clothing. The settlers killed many buffalo. New railroads, roads, and settlements hurt the buffalo habitat. By 1889, the buffalo were nearly extinct.

U.S. soldiers tried to make the Plains Indians give up their land. The Indians fought against the soldiers. Some famous battles were the Battle of the Little Bighorn, the Battle of Wounded Knee, and the Sand Creek Massacre. Finally, the Indians were defeated and forced to move to the reservations.

Government Policy

Government officials wanted to make the Indians live like white settlers. Lawmakers wanted the Indians to assimilate. They tried to force the Indians to give up their culture and traditions. Indians were not allowed to have religious ceremonies. Indian children had to go to special schools. They were not allowed to speak Indian languages. They could not wear Indian clothing.

The government wanted the Indians to become farmers. In 1887, Congress passed the Dawes Act. This law broke reservation land into small pieces. The government gave some pieces to Indians who promised to farm them. It sold the rest of the land to settlers.

Before You Read

Find and underline each vocabulary word.

reservation *noun,* land the government set aside for Indians

habitat *noun,* the area where an animal or plant normally lives or grows

extinct *adjective,* when a certain type of plant or animal no longer exists

assimilate *verb,* to change a group's culture and traditions so that it blends with a larger group

After You Read

REVIEW Why did Plains Indians need large areas of land? Circle reasons why Indians did not want to live on reservations.

REVIEW Why did the buffalo herds shrink? Highlight the sentences that tell how settlers changed the habitat.

REVIEW What did the Dawes Act do to reservation land? Circle the sentence that tells what happened to reservation land.

Practice Book
69   Use with *United States: Civil War to Today,* pp. 186–191

Name _____ Date _____

Reading Skill and Strategy

Reading Skill: Sequence

This skill helps you understand the order in which events happened.

Read "War on the Plains." Then fill in the sequence chart to show the order in which the battles took place.

1.

2.

3.

Reading Strategy: Monitor/Clarify

4. Read "War on the Plains." Why were buffalo important to the Plains

   Indians? _____

5. Read "Government Policy." Name one way in which the government tried to assimilate the American Indians into American culture.

   _____

   _____

   _____

Vocabulary and Study Guide

Vocabulary

Read the clue and write the answer in the blank. Then find the word in the puzzle. Look up, down, forward, and backward. Look for bonus words!

1. The area where an animal or plant normally lives or grows _____

2. When an animal or plant is no longer existing _____

3. To take in a new cultural group and change their culture _____

4. A piece of land that the government has set aside for American Indians _____

Bonus Words: buffalo, nomads

X	N	O	M	A	D	S	N	C	O
E	S	W	I	R	C	S	O	P	Z
B	T	T	O	Y	K	N	I	S	D
I	O	A	T	C	N	I	T	X	E
Q	L	T	L	K	U	L	A	E	T
U	A	I	B	I	N	U	V	H	A
W	F	B	I	O	M	O	R	C	L
W	F	A	P	R	E	I	E	X	O
A	U	H	E	V	N	N	S	R	A
U	B	I	V	A	T	I	E	S	H
N	O	S	D	G	A	F	R	V	A

Study Guide

5. Read "War on the Plains." Then fill in the outline below.

   I. Main Idea: _____

       _____

    A. Supporting Idea: _____

       _____

      1. Detail: _____

      2. Detail: _____

       _____

    B. Supporting Idea: _____

       _____

      1. Detail: _____

       _____

      2. Detail: _____

Use with *United States: Civil War to Today*, pp. 186–191

Summary: The Machine Age

A Time of Invention

In the late 1800s, inventions changed people's lives. They could do more work in less time. E. Remington & Sons made the first typewriter. It saved office workers time. Elijah McCoy invented the oil cup. It dripped oil on machine parts. This helped the parts run longer. Alexander Graham Bell invented the telephone. People in different places could talk to each other. Thomas Edison developed light bulbs. Electric lights kept streets bright at night. Factories and shops could stay open longer.

Big Business

New machines and technologies helped businesses grow. Andrew Carnegie used a new invention to start his steel company. John D. Rockefeller started Standard Oil. The company became a corporation. It bought small companies. This got rid of competition. Standard Oil almost became a monopoly. It owned 90 percent of America's oil. No competition meant consumers had fewer choices. Monopolies could provide poor service or charge higher prices. After making large fortunes, Carnegie and Rockefeller gave millions of dollars to schools, libraries, churches, and hospitals.

Workers' Lives Change

Factories hired many people to run machines. Factory work was boring and dangerous. Workers did the same thing for ten or twelve hours a day. They often worked in unsafe conditions. Factory workers did not make much money. Some families needed more money to survive. They sent their children to work.

Workers formed the American Federation of Labor. They had more power as a group. They wanted businesses to change. Unions wanted safer work conditions. They wanted shorter workdays and better pay. They did not want children to work. Unions used strikes. Businesses fought back. Some strikers were hurt or killed, but labor unions kept fighting for their rights.

Before You Read

Find and underline each vocabulary word.

corporation *noun*, a business in which many people own shares, or parts, of the business

competition *noun*, occurs when more than one business tries to sell the same goods or service

monopoly *noun*, a company that has no competition

American Federation of Labor (AFL) *noun*, an organization of workers originally headed by Samuel Gompers that tried to improve pay and working conditions for its members

strike *noun*, when workers refuse to work in order to force business owners to make changes

After You Read

REVIEW In what ways did inventions of the late 1800s save time? Underline the sentences that tell how inventions helped people.

REVIEW What is a monopoly? Circle the sentences that tell what no competition meant for consumers.

REVIEW Why did workers form labor unions? Highlight changes the unions wanted.

Practice Book
72
Use with *United States: Civil War to Today*, pp. 198–203

Reading Skill and Strategy

Reading Skill: Classify

This skill helps you understand and remember what you have read by organizing facts into groups, or categories.

Read "A Time of Invention." Then fill in the classification chart below. Classify the inventions as work inventions or home inventions. If an invention proved valuable at work and at home, classify it as both.

Work	Home	Both
1.	2.	3.

Reading Strategy: Summarize

4. Read "A Time of Invention." Then check the statement that best summarizes the section.

_____ The phonograph made recorded music possible.

_____ Many new inventions changed the way Americans lived and worked.

_____ The invention of the telephone improved how people communicated.

5. Read "Workers' Lives Change." Then check the statement that best summarizes the section.

_____ Workers formed labor unions to improve their working conditions.

_____ Using machines was less expensive and faster for manufacturing goods.

_____ The goals of the American Federation of Labor included a shorter workday.

Vocabulary and Study Guide

Vocabulary

monopoly	strike	American Federation of Labor (AFL)	corporation	competition

1. As you read the chapter, fill in the details on the branching lines.

Big Business

Mechanization

Study Guide

2. Read "A Time of Invention" and "Big Business." Then fill in the blanks below.

The _____ of the late 1800s improved life by

saving many Americans time and money. One of the most important

of these was the _____, which allowed factories

to stay open after dark. The new inventions helped businesses grow,

One business entrepreneur, _____, formed the

Standard Oil Company. Many people owned parts, or _____,

of the corporation. His company bought other companies, and it

almost became a _____.

3. Read "Workers' Lives Change." Then fill in the blanks below.

Businesses began using machines to make products and needed

many _____. The conditions in factories were often

_____, and the pay was very low. Workers tried to

improve their working _____ by forming labor unions

and going on _____.

Summary: Moving to the United States

Arriving in America

Before 1880, most immigrants living in America came from countries in northern or western Europe. Between 1880 and 1924, about 25 million new immigrants came to the United States. Many came from countries in southern or eastern Europe such as Italy, Russia, Hungary, Greece, and Poland. Some immigrants came looking for jobs. Others were escaping war or persecution. Most immigrants found greater political freedom in the United States. Arriving immigrants had to pass through immigration stations such as Ellis Island in New York Harbor and Angel Island in San Francisco Bay. Government officials asked immigrants about their plans. They were checked for diseases. Many immigrants from China came to the West Coast. Asian immigrants faced more prejudice than European immigrants. More Chinese immigrants were turned away and sent back to China.

Living in a New Country

Immigrants often lived in large cities. Immigrants had their own languages, religions, and customs. They lived in neighborhoods with family or friends that belonged to their ethnic group. Life was hard for immigrants. Many lived in tenements. Many immigrants worked in dangerous factories. Businesses liked to hire immigrants because they worked many hours and were not paid a lot of money. Some Americans worried that immigrants would take their jobs. They did not want immigrants to speak other languages or follow other customs. Immigrants faced prejudice from some Americans. In 1921 and 1924, Congress limited the number of immigrants that could come to the United States.

Immigrants helped to make the United States one of the richest, fastest-growing countries in the world. Immigrants built railroads, dug mines, and worked in factories.

Before You Read

Find and underline each vocabulary word.

persecution *noun*, unfair treatment or punishment

ethnic group *noun*, a group of people who share a culture or language

tenement *noun*, a poorly built apartment building

After You Read

REVIEW **In what ways were Asian immigrants treated differently than immigrants from Europe?** Underline two sentences that tell how immigrants from Asia were treated.

REVIEW **What did immigrants do to help the United States grow?** Highlight the sentence that tells how immigrants helped build the United States.

Reading Skill and Strategy

Reading Skill: Draw Conclusions

Sometimes when you read, you have to figure out things that the writer doesn't tell you. This skill is called drawing conclusions.

Read "Living in a New Country." Then fill in the draw conclusions chart below. Use the statements to draw a conclusion about why Congress kept the Chinese from entering the United States.

Congress decided to limit new immigration.	The Chinese Exclusion Act kept out most people from China.

1. _____

Reading Strategy: Summarize

2. Read "Arriving in America." Then check the statement that best summarizes the section.

_____ After 1880, most immigrants came from Italy, Russia, Hungary, Greece, and Poland.

_____ Ellis Island served as a check-in point for newly arrived immigrants.

_____ In the late 1800s and early 1900s, many immigrants came to the United States.

3. Read "Living in a New Country." Then complete the summary.

Many immigrants moved to _____ and worked

_____. Immigrants usually could only afford to live in

rundown buildings called _____.

Vocabulary and Study Guide

Vocabulary

Write the definition of each vocabulary word below.

1. tenement _____

2. persecution _____

3. ethnic group _____

_____

4. Use one of the words in a sentence. _____

_____

_____

Study Guide

Read "Arriving in America." Then fill in the Venn diagram below.

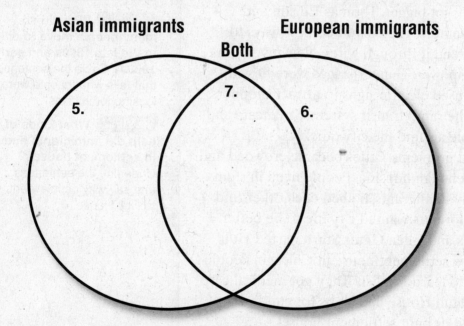

Asian immigrants   Both   European immigrants

5.   7.   6.

Read "Living in a New Country." Then answer the question.

8. Write two reasons why some Americans wanted to stop immigration.

_____

_____

_____

77   Use with *United States: Civil War to Today,* pp. 206–209

Summary: Big Cities

Moving to Cities

Many people moved to cities in the late 1800s and early 1900s. Many immigrants lived in cities. People who lived on farms also moved to the city. Machines were used on many farms. Fewer workers were needed. People moved to cities to find jobs. Cities grew very fast. Urbanization was taking place in some cities. By 1920, over half of all Americans lived in a city.

Chicago was a city that grew quickly. It was in a good place. Chicago is near Lake Michigan. Canals linked Chicago to the Mississippi and Illinois rivers. Railroads and boats brought natural resources to the city. Logs were shipped to factories. Machines cut the logs into lumber. Wheat and corn were also shipped to Chicago. Mills turned them into food. Cows and pigs were sent to stockyards.

Changes in Cities

Cities changed as they got bigger. Thomas Edison and Nikola Tesla were inventors. They invented new ways to make electricity and send it through wires. New inventions needed electricity for power. Theater stages were lit with electric lights. Stores used electric signs to attract shoppers. Electricity powered the rapid transit system. Streetcars and subways moved people around the city quickly.

Growing cities had problems. Cities became crowded and noisy. There was not enough housing. People lived in slums. City people, especially immigrants, helped each other find housing and jobs. Reformers wanted city life to be better. In 1889, Jane Addams and Ellen Gates Starr started Hull House. This was a new settlement house in Chicago. People came to Hull House to learn English. They got medical care and looked for jobs. Hull House had clubs for children. Reformers in other cities built settlement houses.

Before You Read

Find and underline each vocabulary word.

urbanization *noun*, the growth of cities

rapid transit *noun*, a system of trains used to move people around cities

slum *noun*, a poor, crowded part of a city

Hull House *noun*, one of the first settlement houses in the United States

settlement house *noun*, a community center for people in cities

After You Read

REVIEW Why did so many people move to cities in the late 1800s and early 1900s? Circle the sentence that tells what people were looking for in cities.

REVIEW What kinds of help did immigrants find in settlement houses? Underline the sentences that say why people went to Hull House.

Reading Skill and Strategy

Reading Skill: Cause and Effect

This skill helps you see how one event can be related to another, either by causing it or resulting from it.

Read "Moving to Cities." Then fill in the cause-and-effect chart below to show why Chicago's location helped its population grow.

Cause	Effect
1.	Almost 10 times as many people lived in Chicago in 1920 than in 1870.

Reading Strategy: Summarize

2. Read "Moving to Cities." Then complete the summary.

In the late 1800s and early 1990s, cities in the United States

grew quickly because _____

_____.

_____

3. Read "Changes in Cities." Then write a short summary.

_____

_____

_____

Vocabulary and Study Guide

Vocabulary

If you do not know a word's meaning, try breaking it into smaller parts.
It may contain a smaller word that you know.

Find the smaller words inside these words. Use what you know about the
smaller word or words to write the meaning of the longer word.

New word	Words in it that I know	Word meanings that I know	What I think the word means
1. urbanization			
2. rapid transit			
3. settlement house			

4. Write the definition of *slum* below.

_____

Study Guide

Read "Moving to Cities." Then fill in the cause-and-effect chart below.

Cause

5. New _____ took jobs away from people on farms. →

Effect

6. [box]

Read "Changes in Cities." Then answer the questions.

7. Name two technologies that changed the way cities looked and

worked. Give an example of each one. _____

_____

8. What made tenements unsafe? _____

_____

Name _____ Date _____

Summary: Changes for the Better

The Progressives

In the early 1900s, industrialization led many adults and children to work in unsafe factories. Factories polluted cities. Progressives wanted to make factories and cities safer. They fought for labor laws to end child labor and protect factory workers.

Upton Sinclair was a muckraker. He wrote a book about the dangers of meat factories. In 1906, President Theodore Roosevelt worked with Congress to pass two laws. The Pure Food and Drug Act and the Meat Inspection Act said that medicine and foods had to be made without harmful chemicals and in clean factories.

President Theodore Roosevelt also set aside millions of acres of land for national parks and wilderness areas. Austin Peay, a reform-minded governor of Tennessee, pushed for legislation to buy land for the Great Smoky Mountains National Park.

Working for Equal Rights

Women fought for many years for the right to vote. One woman, Anne Dallas Dudley of Tennessee, gave speeches and wrote letters to lawmakers. In 1920, the Nineteenth Amendment passed, giving women the right to vote.

In the early 1900s, African Americans, Mexican Americans, American Indians, and Asian Americans faced prejudice when they tried to get jobs or places to live. Some states did not allow African Americans and other groups to vote and forced their children to go to different schools.

In 1909, the National Association for the Advancement of Colored People (NAACP) was founded. "Colored People" was a term then used for African Americans. The NAACP worked for equality. It wanted African Americans to be treated fairly. W.E.B. Du Bois wrote about African American life. He helped people see why laws should be changed. Ida B. Wells, a newspaper writer in Tennessee, wrote about the unfair treatment of African Americans. Booker T. Washington started a school to educate African Americans.

Between 1910 and 1930, about 1.5 million African Americans moved to northern cities to work in factories and businesses. This was called the Great Migration.

Before You Read

Find and underline each vocabulary word.

industrialization *noun,* the growth of industry

progressives *noun,* reformers who thought governments should make labor laws

labor laws *noun,* laws that protect workers

muckraker *noun,* someone who "rakes up," or points out, unpleasant truths

After You Read

REVIEW What did the Pure Food and Drug Act and the Meat Inspection Act do to make food safer? Circle the sentence that tells you the answer.

REVIEW What is the NAACP and what is its purpose? Circle the words that tell what NAACP means. Underline two sentences that say what the NAACP worked for.

81 Use with *United States: Civil War to Today,* pp. 216–219

Reading Skill and Strategy

Reading Skill: Problem and Solution

This skill helps you see what problem some people faced and how they resolved it.

Read "The Progressives." Then fill in the problem-and-solution chart below to show the problem that made each solution necessary.

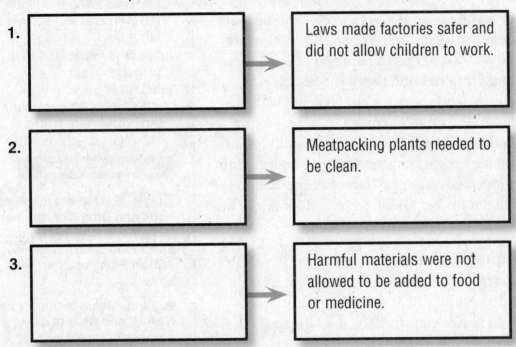

1. [ ] → Laws made factories safer and did not allow children to work.

2. [ ] → Meatpacking plants needed to be clean.

3. [ ] → Harmful materials were not allowed to be added to food or medicine.

Reading Strategy: Summarize

4. Read "Changes for the Better." Then write a short summary of each section.

Section 1: The Progressives

Summary: _____

_____

_____

Section 2: Working for Equal Rights

Summary: _____

_____

_____

Vocabulary and Study Guide

Vocabulary

Write the vocabulary word that matches each definition.

1. The growth of industry _____

2. Reformers who wanted to make new laws and improve society

   _____

3. Laws that protect workers _____

4. Someone who points out unpleasant truths _____

Use *progressives* and *muckraker* in sentences.

5. _____

   _____

6. _____

   _____

Study Guide

7. Read "Changes for the Better." Then read each description. In the box, write the name of the person described.

I was an African American writer and a leader of the NAACP.	I am >	
I gave speeches and wrote letters to lawmakers about women's suffrage.	I am >	
I started schools to give southern African Americans education and job training.	I am >	
I set aside land for national parks and worked with Congress to pass safe-food laws.	I am >	

Use with *United States: Civil War to Today*, pp. 216–219

Skillbuilder: Identify Fact and Opinion

Practice

Read the following statements. Then identify each one as a fact or an opinion. Explain how you made your decision. Look at the steps in "Learn the Skill" on page 222 for help.

1. By 1900, Andrew Carnegie's steel company produced one quarter of all the steel made in the United States. _____

   _____

2. Child labor was probably the worst problem the United States faced in the late 1800s. _____

3. It seems to me that the immigrants should have been treated better since they worked extremely hard in often dangerous situations.

   _____

4. The inventions of steel frames and electric elevators in the late 1800s made the building of skyscrapers possible. _____

   _____

Apply

Read "Making Changes" on page 217. Write one fact and one opinion from your reading. Then explain why each is a fact or opinion.

5. Fact statement: _____

   _____

   Explanation: _____

   _____

6. Opinion statement: _____

   _____

   Explanation: _____

   _____

Name _____ Date _____

Almanac Map Practice

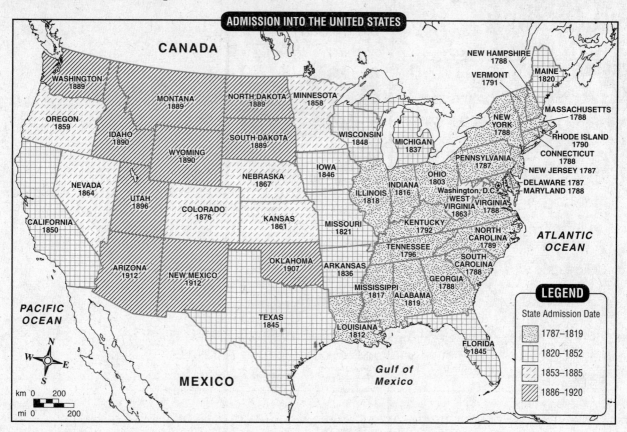

ADMISSION INTO THE UNITED STATES

LEGEND
State Admission Date
1787–1819
1820–1852
1853–1885
1886–1920

Use the map to do these activities and answer these questions.

Practice

1. In which year did the most states join the Union? _____

2. Circle the states that joined the Union in 1889.

3. Draw a box around the state that joined the Union in 1907.

4. Write the name of each state that borders the boxed state. Then list

   the year in which each of these states joined the Union. _____

   _____

   _____

Apply

5. Work with a partner to identify the year your state joined the Union.
   Then figure out how many states joined before your state and how
   many joined after it. Note: Alaska and Hawaii became states in 1959.

_____

85   Use with *United States: Civil War to Today,* pp. 230–231

Almanac Graph Practice

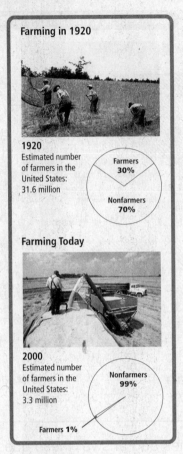

Farming in 1920

1920
Estimated number
of farmers in the
United States:
31.6 million

Farmers
30%

Nonfarmers
70%

Farming Today

2000
Estimated number
of farmers in the
United States:
3.3 million

Nonfarmers
99%

Farmers 1%

Practice

1. Were there more farmers or nonfarmers during the 1920s?

_____

2. What happened to the number of farmers between 1920 and 2000?

_____

Apply

3. Use the information below to complete the pie graphs.

1960	2000
Americans working in goods-producing jobs: 38% Americans working in service jobs: 62%	Americans working in goods-producing jobs: 20% Americans working in service jobs: 80%

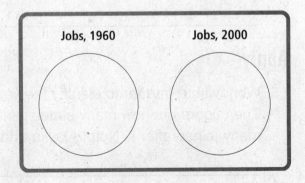

Jobs, 1960   Jobs, 2000

Practice Book
86
Use with *United States: Civil War to Today*, p. 231

Summary: The Nation Expands

The Nation Expands

Through the 1800s, the United States gained new land in western North America. In 1867, the United States bought Alaska from Russia. Alaska was rich in fish, forests, and minerals. In 1912, Alaska became a U.S. territory.

In the late 1800s, American settlers in Hawaii owned most of the sugar and pineapple plantations and land there. The Hawaiian ruler, Queen Liliuokalani, wanted power and land returned to her people. The American settlers in Hawaii forced the queen from power in 1893. Then they asked to join the United States. In 1898, Hawaii became a U.S. territory.

The Spanish-American War

Some American leaders believed in imperialism. They wanted more land and colonies. The nation would gain more land after the Spanish-American War. In 1895, the Spanish colony of Cuba revolted against Spain. American newspapers wrote stories about how Spain treated Cubans cruelly during the revolt. These stories were yellow journalism because they were shocking and not always true.

In February 1898, the U.S. Navy ship *Maine* exploded in a Cuban harbor. Americans blamed Spain, and Congress declared war on Spain. In August 1898, Spain surrendered and agreed to give Puerto Rico, the Philippines, and Guam to the United States. These countries became territories of the United States. Cuba became independent.

Building the Panama Canal

President Theodore Roosevelt wanted to build a canal to link the Atlantic and Pacific Oceans. A canal would shorten the trip from the east coast to the west coast. This would save time and money. The best place for the canal was at the Isthmus of Panama, the narrowest point in Central America. Panama was part of the nation of Colombia. Colombia did not want to sell Panama. Roosevelt helped Panama win independence from Colombia. The new leaders of Panama let the United States build the canal. The Panama Canal opened in 1914.

Before You Read

Find and underline each vocabulary word.

imperialism *noun*, when nations build empires by adding colonies

yellow journalism *noun*, a kind of writing that exaggerates news to shock and attract readers

isthmus *noun*, a narrow strip of land with water on both sides that links two larger pieces of land

After You Read

REVIEW How did Alaska become a U.S. territory? Underline the words that tell the answer.

REVIEW What was the effect of the explosion of the *Maine*? Draw a box around the sentence that tells the answer.

REVIEW Why did the United States build the Panama Canal? Circle two sentences that tell the answer.

Practice Book
87   Use with *United States: Civil War to Today*, pp. 234–239

Reading Skill and Strategy

Reading Skill: Compare and Contrast

This skill helps you understand how historical events or people are similar and different.

Read "The Nation Expands." Then fill in the chart below to compare and contrast Alaska and Hawaii.

Alaska	Hawaii	Both
1.	2.	3.

Reading Strategy: Question

4. Read "The Nation Expands." Then check the question that you might ask while reading this section.

____ What made Alaska so valuable?

____ Before Alaska, what had been the largest U.S. territory?

____ How much money did the United States pay for Hawaii?

5. Read "The Spanish-American War." Then check the question that you might ask while reading this section.

____ What was left of France's overseas empire by 1890?

____ How did the U.S. navy help the United States win the war?

____ Why was Theodore Roosevelt considered a hero after the Spanish-American War?

Vocabulary and Study Guide

Vocabulary

Write the definition of each vocabulary word below.

1. yellow journalism _____

_____

2. isthmus _____

_____

3. imperialism _____

_____

4. Use two of the words in a sentence. _____

_____

_____

Study Guide

Read "The Nation Expands." Then choose the correct ending to each statement below.

5. Alaska was a valuable purchase for the United States because of its

    A. mountain ranges.   **B.** fish, forests, and minerals.   **C.** gold.

6. Plantation owners in Hawaii wanted to

    A. stay in control.   **B.** give control to Hawaiians.   **C.** leave Hawaii.

Read "The Spanish-American War." Then fill in the sequence chart below.

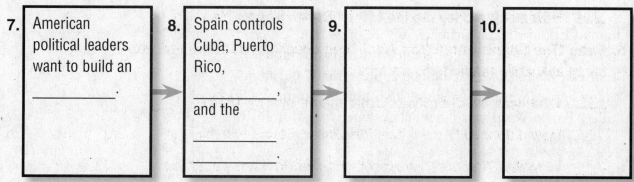

7. American political leaders want to build an _____ .

8. Spain controls Cuba, Puerto Rico, _____ , and the _____ .

9.

10.

Summary: World War I

Causes of the War

In the 1900s, nationalism made countries such as Germany, Russia, and France compete for land and power. Some nations practiced imperialism and started colonies. Nations wanted to protect their empires, so they made their armies and navies stronger. Militarism became popular in Europe.

Countries also made alliances with one another. The two most important alliances were the Allied Powers (or Allies), and the Central Powers. In 1914, a Serbian killed Archduke Franz Ferdinand, a member of Austria's royal family. Austria-Hungary responded by declaring war on Serbia. Russia and Serbia had an alliance, so Russia joined the war to help Serbia. Then Germany, a Central Power, declared war on Russia. Because of their alliances, many countries were pulled into the war. It was the start of World War I.

America Enters the War

At first, most Americans did not want the United States to join the war. Then in 1915, Germany sank the *Lusitania,* a British passenger ship that was carrying many Americans. Americans were angry, but Germany promised not to attack more passenger ships. In 1917, Germany broke its promise and attacked American ships. The United States declared war on the Central Powers.

Both sides used new ways of fighting and new weapons. Thousands of men fought and died in trench warfare. Armies used poison gas, machine guns, hand grenades, and cannons that fired large shells through the air. They fought using airplanes, submarines, and army tanks.

The war made many heroes. One was an American pilot named Eddie Rickenbacker. Many Tennesseans served in the war. Alvin C. York was one of the most famous Tennesseans to serve. He helped capture many Germans. Many heroes were never famous. Millions of soldiers were killed. World War I was the most destructive war in history at that time.

Before You Read

Find and underline each vocabulary word.

nationalism *noun,* the belief that your country deserves more success than others

militarism *noun,* the building of a strong military to frighten or defeat other countries

alliance *noun,* an agreement nations make to support and defend each other

trench warfare *noun,* fighting by soldiers on both sides from long narrow ditches called trenches

After You Read

REVIEW **Why did so many countries join the war?** Underline the sentence that tells the answer.

REVIEW **What caused the United States to enter the war?** Draw a box around the sentence that tells the answer.

Reading Skill and Strategy

Reading Skill: Sequence

This skill helps you understand the order in which events happened.

Read "America Enters the War." Then fill in the chart below to show the order in which the United States entered World War I.

1.	Germany sank a British ship with Americans on board.
2.	
3.	
4.	

Reading Strategy: Question

5. Read "Causes of the War." Then check the question that you might ask while reading this section.

_____ Why were France and Britain enemies of the United States?

_____ How did national alliances lead to World War I?

_____ When did Mexico join the Central Powers?

6. Read "America Enters the War." Then complete the answer to the question.

Question: What new weapons were used during World War I?

Answer: The Allies and the Central Powers fought with _____

_____

_____

Vocabulary and Study Guide

Vocabulary

1. Draw a line connecting the vocabulary word to its meaning.

nationalism	an agreement nations make to support and defend each other
militarism	the belief that your country deserves more success than others
trench warfare	building a strong military to frighten or defeat other countries
alliance	when soldiers fight from long, narrow ditches

Study Guide

2. Read "Causes of the War" and "America Enters the War." Then fill in the blanks below.

Imperialism, nationalism, and _____ led to World War I. The Central Powers and the _____ were the two _____ in Europe involved in the war. World War I soldiers lived and fought in _____ on the battlefield. Most Americans wanted to stay out of the war, but when _____ began attacking American _____, the United States declared war on the Central Powers. Soldiers used new technologies, such as tanks, submarines, _____ dropped from planes, and _____ gas, for the first time.

Skillbuilder: Understand Perspective

"I am bitterly opposed to my country entering the war,…War brings no prosperity to the great mass of common and patriotic citizens…We are taking a step today that is fraught with [full of] untold danger…We are going to run the risk of sacrificing millions of our countrymen's lives."

— *Senator George W. Norris*

"We know that in such a government [as Germany's]…we can never have a friend; and that in the presence of its organized power…there can be no assured security for the democratic governments of the world…The world must be made safe for democracy."

—*President Woodrow Wilson*

Practice

1. Which speaker opposes U.S. involvement in World War I?

_____

2. Summarize Senator Norris's perspective.

_____

_____

_____

3. How might his job as President affect Woodrow Wilson's perspective on

entering World War I? _____

_____

Apply

Think about a conflict you have faced in your life. Write a paragraph explaining your perspective and the other perspective.

_____

_____

_____

Summary: The Home Front

Life on the Home Front

Soldiers needed many things to fight World War I. The U.S. government created more supplies for soldiers by putting rations on civilian goods, such as meat. The things people did not use were given to soldiers. The government used propaganda to remind people to help with the war.

Many men were fighting in Europe. The factories needed new workers. Thousands of African Americans left the South to take factory jobs in the North. Women also took new jobs. Women worked in jobs that men had normally done, such as making weapons and repairing cars. Their efforts convinced many people that women should have their right to vote recognized. In 1920, women could finally vote.

The War Ends

In 1917, the United States joined World War I. About one million American soldiers went to France. After losing many battles, the Central Powers realized they could not win. They signed an armistice. The war ended in 1918.

In 1919, Allied leaders met in France to write a treaty. Some European leaders blamed Germany for the fighting in western Europe. These leaders used the Treaty of Versailles to punish Germany. The treaty forced Germany to give up its overseas colonies, give land to France, and pay money to Allied nations.

The treaty also created the League of Nations. President Wilson thought the League would help prevent war by solving problems peacefully. The United States Senate refused to approve the Treaty of Versailles. The Senate worried that the United States might get pulled into more wars if they joined the League of Nations.

Americans were upset by the deaths and destruction of World War I. They wanted the United States to stay out of world conflicts. Some began to believe in isolationism.

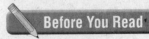

Before You Read

Find and underline each vocabulary word.

rations *noun,* limits on the amounts of goods civilians could have

propaganda *noun,* information that is used to shape people's thinking

armistice *noun,* an agreement to stop fighting

isolationism *noun,* a desire to stay out of world events

After You Read

REVIEW **Which two groups of Americans took new jobs during World War I?** Underline two sentences that tell the answer.

REVIEW **What effect did the Treaty of Versailles have on Germany?** Circle the sentence that tells the answer.

Reading Skill and Strategy

Reading Skill: Problem and Solution

This skill helps you see what problem some people faced and how they resolved it.

Read "The War Effort." Then fill in the problem-and-solution chart below. How did the country fill jobs during the war?

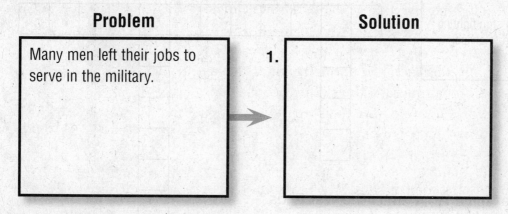

Problem

Many men left their jobs to serve in the military.

Solution

1.

Reading Strategy: Question

2. Read "Life on the Home Front." Then write a question for the answer.

Answer: African Americans and women stepped up and did the jobs.

Question: _____

_____

_____

3. Read "The War Ends." Then write a question and the answer to it.

Question: _____

_____

Answer: _____

_____

_____

Vocabulary and Study Guide

Vocabulary

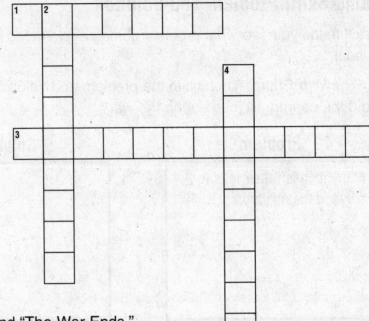

Across

1. Limits on the amount of goods people could have
3. Staying out of world events

Down

2. An agreement to stop fighting
4. Information used to shape people's thinking

Study Guide

Read "Life on the Home Front" and "The War Ends."
Then fill in the chart below.

Causes		Effects
Women performed well in jobs that had been held by men.	5.	
The Central Powers signed an armistice.	6.	
The Allies win the war and write the Treaty of Versailles.	7.	

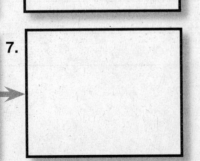

Summary: An Economic Boom

Changes in Production

After World War I, Americans elected Warren G. Harding to be President. He believed Americans were tired of war. He said Americans should stop thinking about war and go back to their homes and jobs.

After the war ended, there was an economic boom in the United States. The United States became the richest country in the world. Many Americans earned enough money to buy homes.

Henry Ford's factories began to use mass production to make cars. Mass production means using machines to make many of the same products at the same time. Each worker or group of workers on an assembly line did one job. This way of organizing work is called division of labor. It allowed Ford to make cars more quickly and cheaply than before.

Mass production changed the economy because it helped industries grow. As they grew, they hired more workers. The workers earned more money and bought more goods. People often bought goods such as radios and washing machines on credit.

Many Americans invested their money. They bought stocks in different companies on the stock market. They hoped they could sell the stock at a higher price to make a profit. Other people put their money into savings accounts at banks. Banks lent money to businesses to help them grow.

Government in the 1920s

The United States elected three Presidents in the 1920s: Warren G. Harding, Calvin Coolidge, and Herbert Hoover. All three Presidents were Republicans. They all wanted the U.S. economy to grow even stronger. Coolidge wanted the government to work like a business. His government collected more money than it spent. He also cut taxes so people would have more money to spend and invest.

In 1929, Herbert Hoover became President. He thought the government should not do too much to make the economy strong. He believed that real economic growth came from the hard work of ordinary people. In the 1920s, people thought prosperity would last forever.

Before You Read

Find and underline each vocabulary word.

economic boom *noun*, a period of fast economic growth

division of labor *noun*, when workers perform different parts of a large task

credit *noun*, a plan that allows buyers to take their purchases home and pay for them over time

stock *noun*, a share of ownership in a company

stock market *noun*, a place where stocks are bought and sold

After You Read

REVIEW **In what way did mass production change the economy?** Underline the sentences that tell the answer.

REVIEW **How did Calvin Coolidge encourage economic growth?** Highlight the sentences that tell how Coolidge wanted the government to work.

Reading Skill and Strategy

Reading Skill: Predict Outcomes

This skill allows you to think about what might happen, based on what you have read.

Read the section "The Automobile Industry." In the first box, write what you think happened to the way other industries made their products. In the second box, write how industry grew.

Prediction

1.

Outcome

2.

Reading Strategy: Predict and Infer

3. Read "An Economic Boom." Then check the best inference.

____ After the boom, many people could afford to buy cars.

____ Airplanes made traveling very easy in the decade after World War I.

____ In the 1920s, people spent all of their money buying consumer goods.

4. Read "Government in the 1920s." Then check the best inference.

____ President Hoover tried to involve the government in the economy.

____ Presidents Harding, Coolidge, and Hoover made the economy worse.

____ President Coolidge wanted the government to spend less than the taxes it collected.

Practice Book
98 Use with *United States: Civil War to Today*, pp. 260–263

Name _____ Date _____

Vocabulary and Study Guide

Vocabulary

Write the definition of each vocabulary word below.

1. economic boom _____

2. stock _____

3. stock market _____

4. division of labor _____

5. credit _____

_____

6. Use *division of labor* in a sentence.

_____

_____

Study Guide

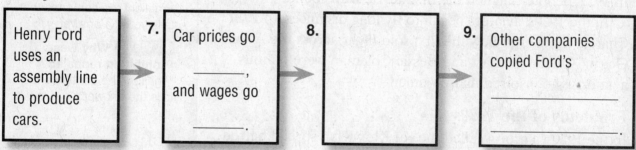

| Henry Ford uses an assembly line to produce cars. | **7.** Car prices go _____, and wages go _____. | **8.** | **9.** Other companies copied Ford's _____ _____ |

Read "Government in the 1920s." Then fill in the sequence chart below.

Calvin Coolidge	Herbert Hoover
10.	**11.**

Practice Book

99

Use with *United States: Civil War to Today*, pp. 260–263

Summary: The 1920s

Technology Changes Lives

During World War I, many Americans moved to cities. They worked in factories or other businesses. Technology changed American lives. Many people bought cars. Electricity made people's lives easier. It made doing household chores easier and gave people more free time.

A Changing Society

During the 1920s, or the "Roaring Twenties," women did things they did not do before. They worked outside their homes. They went to college and played sports. Most important, they won the right to vote.

Music changed, too. Jazz began among African Americans in the South. Harlem, a neighborhood in New York City, was famous for jazz, art, and literature.

America's first radio broadcast was in 1920. Soon many families owned radios. Families sat together and listened to news reports, music, sports, mystery stories, and comedy shows. In 1927, people watched the first movie with sound.

In the 1920s, aviators began to fly long distances. In 1927, Charles Lindbergh flew the first solo flight across the Atlantic Ocean. Amelia Earhart and Bessie Coleman were famous aviators who inspired many women.

Problems of the 1920s

In the 1920s, a group called the Ku Klux Klan spread hatred and prejudice against African Americans and other groups. Klan members attacked and sometimes killed people they thought were "un-American."

In 1919, the Eighteenth Amendment to the Constitution was ratified. It made selling and drinking alcohol against the law. This was called Prohibition. Criminals made and sold alcohol. Illegal activities led to violence. In 1933, the government ended Prohibition.

After World War I ended, the Allies did not need American crops. Some farmers could not earn enough to pay back money they borrowed. Many had to sell their farms.

Before You Read

Find and underline each vocabulary word.

broadcast *noun,* a program sent out over a radio or television station

aviator *noun,* a person who flies an airplane

prohibition *noun,* the act of forbidding something

After You Read

REVIEW What were two ways women's lives changed during the 1920s? Circle three sentences that tell about things women did.

REVIEW What kinds of radio programs did people listen to during the 1920s? Highlight the sentence that tells you the answer.

REVIEW Why was Prohibition repealed? Highlight the sentence that tells the answer.

Reading Skill and Strategy

Reading Skill: Main Idea and Details

This skill helps you understand events by seeing how they are related.

Read "Problems of the 1920s." Then fill in the chart below. Write details that support the main idea on the lines.

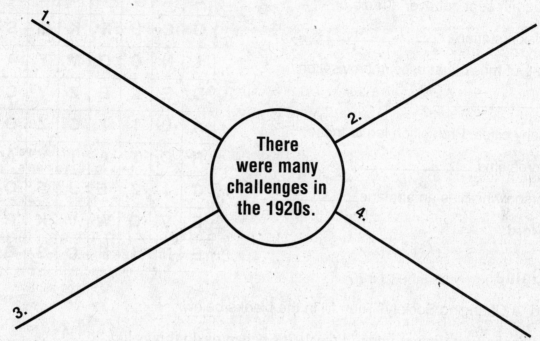

1.

2.

3.

4.

There were many challenges in the 1920s.

Reading Strategy: Predict and Infer

5. Read "A Changing Society." Then check the best inference.

____ Women had more political power in the 1920s than ever before.

____ The style of jazz greatly influenced the future of country and western music.

____ Radio entertainment first became popular in the late 1930s.

6. Read "Problems of the 1920s." Then complete the inference.

Criminals could sell alcohol for a high price during Prohibition

because _____.

Vocabulary and Study Guide

Vocabulary

Solve the clue and write the answer in the blank. Then find the word in the puzzle. Look up, down, forward, and backward. Look for a bonus word!

1. A program sent out over a radio or

   television station _____

2. A style of music that uses improvisation

   _____

3. In many cities, Prohibition led to these

   two problems _____

4. A person who flies an airplane _____

Bonus Word: _____

Z	E	L	I	O	Z	T	O
O	C	L	N	K	G	S	H
I	N	G	O	M	Y	A	T
D	E	L	E	Z	Y	C	R
A	L	I	T	C	Z	D	C
R	O	T	A	I	V	A	N
C	I	Z	E	J	E	O	J
E	V	Q	W	V	K	R	E
E	M	I	R	C	S	B	M

Study Guide

5. Read "A Changing Society." Then fill in the blanks below.

   For the first time, women in the 1920s began to do things like

   play _____, work outside the home, and go to college.

   _____ music became very popular and America's

   first _____ allowed people to hear news, music, and

   sports events at home. Charles Lindbergh became the first person to

   _____ alone across the _____.

Read "Problems of the 1920s." Then fill in the cause-and-effect chart below.

Causes	Effects
Some Americans were prejudiced against anyone different.	6. _____
During the Prohibition Era, criminals made and sold alcohol.	7. _____

Use with *United States: Civil War to Today,* pp. 266–271

Summary: The Great Depression

The Economic Depression

During the 1920s, many Americans did not think the economic boom would end. They borrowed money to buy goods and to invest in the stock market. Then, in October 1929, the stock market crashed. The crash led to an economic bust. The value of stocks dropped. Many people and businesses lost money.

The economy got worse. Stores could not sell their goods, so factories did not need as many workers. Businesses closed, and many people lost their jobs. Unemployment was high. This time of unemployment and hardship is called the Great Depression. It lasted through the 1930s.

Many people, especially farmers, were in debt. They could not buy as many homes or consumer goods as before. Many banks closed and customers lost their savings. Banks could not make loans to help businesses.

Hard Times for Americans

The Great Depression caused hardship for Americans. In 1932, about 25 percent of the working population did not have jobs. People without jobs lost their homes because they could not pay their debts. Many became homeless and built shanties. The shanties were homes made from cardboard, broken cars, and wood scraps. There were shantytowns all across the United States. People also called these shantytowns Hoovervilles, after President Herbert Hoover. They blamed him for the economic problems.

People were poor and hungry. They stood in bread lines at community kitchens to get free meals. Charities gave food to needy people. The Great Depression was very hard on tenant farmers in the South. These farmers paid rent or a share of the crops they grew to the landowners. During the Depression, many of them had no money for rent, so they had to leave.

In the early 1930s, there was a bad drought on the Great Plains. Almost no rain fell, and the soil turned to dust. People called this area the Dust Bowl. Many farmers left their farms. Artists, such as Dorothea Lange and Woody Guthrie, expressed suffering during the Great Depression through photographs, music, and writing.

 Before You Read

Find and underline each vocabulary word.

economic bust *noun*, an extreme downturn in the economy

unemployment *noun*, the number of people who are looking for a job but can't find one

Great Depression *noun*, the period in U.S. history when many people couldn't find work and many businesses closed

debt *noun*, money that one person owes to another

charity *noun*, an organization that helps people in need

After You Read

REVIEW Why did factory workers lose their jobs during the Great Depression? Draw a box around two sentences that tell the answer.

REVIEW Why did people build shantytowns and stand in bread lines during the Great Depression? Circle two sentences that tell why people lost their homes and built shantytowns. Underline two sentences that tell why people stood in bread lines.

103   Use with *United States: Civil War to Today*, pp. 274–277

Reading Skill and Strategy

Reading Skill: Cause and Effect

This skill helps you see how one event can be related to another, either by causing it or resulting from it.

Read "The Impact on Farmers." What was the effect of the severe drought?

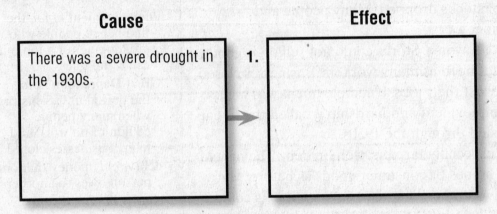

Cause

There was a severe drought in the 1930s.

Effect

1.

Reading Strategy: Predict and Infer

2. Read "The Economic Depression." Then complete the statement.

   The failure of banks hurt the economy because _____

   _____.

3. Look over "Hard Times for Americans." Then make a prediction about what the section will be about.

   _____

   _____

4. Read "Hard Times for Americans." Then explain why tenant farmers and sharecroppers could not pay their rent during the Depression.

   _____

   _____

Vocabulary and Study Guide

Vocabulary

1. Draw a line connecting the vocabulary word to its meaning.

debt	the number of people who cannot find jobs
economic bust	the period in U.S. history when many people couldn't find work and businesses closed
charity	an extreme downturn in the economy
unemployment	money that one person owes to another
Great Depression	a group that helps people in need

Study Guide

2. Read "Hard Times for Americans." Then fill in the outline below.

   I. Main Idea: The Depression caused hardship for Americans.

   A. Supporting Idea: The Depression was especially hard on farmers.

   1. Detail: _____

   2. Detail: _____

   _____

   B. Supporting Idea: Artists expressed the suffering during the Depression through their art.

   1. Detail: _____

   _____

   2. Detail: _____

   _____

Use with *United States: Civil War to Today*, pp. 274–277

Skillbuilder: Read Population Maps

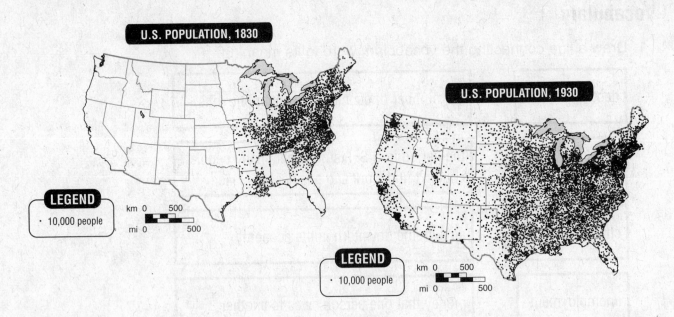

Practice

1. What part of the country had the largest number of people in 1930?

_____

2. Compare the two maps. Then explain how settlements in the United

States changed between 1830 and 1930. _____

_____

_____

3. Some places on the 1830 map have no dots at all. Does that mean

that no one was living there? _____

_____

Apply

Read "Hard Times for Americans" in Lesson 3. Look at the 1930
population map. How did the hard times affect the population of the
western United States?

_____

_____

Summary: The New Deal

The Election of 1932

Herbert Hoover was President when the Great Depression began. Hoover believed the economy would get better by itself. But the economy did not get better. It got worse. More people lost their homes and jobs.

Americans wanted the government to help. Congress passed laws that loaned money to banks and railroads, but these laws did not improve the whole economy.

In 1933, Franklin D. Roosevelt became President. Roosevelt thought the federal government should help end the Depression. He promised to give the people a "new deal" by creating programs to help them.

The New Deal

President Roosevelt soon started government programs to give food and shelter to the needy. These programs were known as the New Deal. The Civilian Conservation Corps, or CCC, gave people jobs that conserved, or protected, the natural environment. CCC workers planted trees and cleared hiking trails.

The Tennessee Valley Authority, or TVA, gave people jobs building dams on the Tennessee River. These dams created hydroelectricity for rural areas. The dams also prevented floods. The Works Progress Administration, or WPA, gave people jobs building streets, parks, libraries, and schools.

These New Deal programs helped all Americans and gave jobs to millions of people. Many New Deal programs continue today. The Social Security Act provides money to people who are over 65 years old or who have disabilities.

The New Deal made regulations to try to prevent another depression. Federal bank regulations protect people's savings accounts. Another regulation protects workers by setting a national minimum wage.

By 1939, many Americans still did not have jobs, but the economy was improving. Since Roosevelt's presidency, the federal government has been a bigger part of Americans' lives.

Before You Read

Find and underline each vocabulary word.

hydroelectricity *noun*, electricity produced by moving water

Social Security *noun*, a program that provides money to Americans over the age of 65 or who have disabilities and cannot work

regulation *noun*, a rule or a law

minimum wage *noun*, the lowest amount of money most workers can be paid per hour

After You Read

REVIEW How were Hoover's and Roosevelt's views about the federal government different? Circle the sentence that tells Hoover's view. Draw a box around the sentence that tells Roosevelt's view.

REVIEW What does the Social Security Act do? Highlight the sentence that tells you the answer.

Practice Book

107

Use with *United States: Civil War to Today*, pp. 282–285

Reading Skill and Strategy

Reading Skill: Draw Conclusions

Sometimes when you read, you have to figure out things that the writer doesn't tell you. This skill is called drawing conclusions.

Read "Eleanor Roosevelt." Then fill in the chart below. How did she try to help the country?

Eleanor Roosevelt traveled all over the country.	Eleanor Roosevelt believed government should help people.	Eleanor Roosevelt spoke out for the rights of workers, women, African Americans, and children.

1.

Reading Strategy: Predict and Infer

2. Look over "The New Deal." Read the headings and scan the photographs. Then make a prediction about what each section will be about.

   Heading 1: The Election of 1932

   Prediction: _____

   _____

   Heading 2: The New Deal

   Prediction: _____

   _____

Vocabulary and Study Guide

Vocabulary

Write the definition of each vocabulary word below.

1. hydroelectricity _____

2. Social Security _____

_____

3. regulation _____

4. minimum wage _____

_____

5. Use *regulation* and *minimum wage* in a sentence.

_____

_____

Study Guide

Read "The Election of 1932." Then choose the correct ending to each statement below.

6. President Hoover believed government should not try to change the

   A. business laws.   **B.** economy.   **C.** railroads.

7. Franklin Delano Roosevelt promised that his government would

   A. take action.   **B.** end regulations.   **C.** conserve resources.

Read "The New Deal." Then fill in the main idea and details chart below with details that support the main idea.

> **The federal government created programs called the New Deal to help Americans during the Great Depression.**

8. [ ]   9. [ ]   10. [ ]

Name _____ Date _____

UNIT 5

Almanac Map Practice

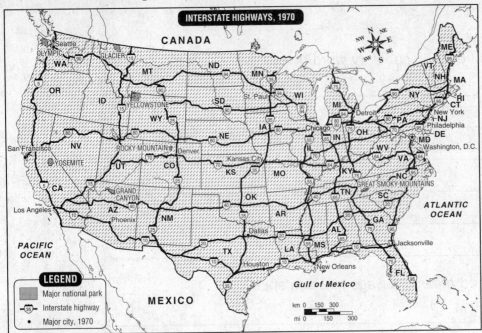

Use the map to do these activities and answer these questions.

Practice

1. Which interstate highway passes through Houston? _____

2. Use a crayon or marker to trace Interstate 80 from San Francisco to the city where it ends in the East.

3. Circle the city that is located at the intersection of Interstate Highways 25 and 70.

4. If a family living in Montana wanted to visit Seattle, which interstate highway would they most likely use? _____

Apply

5. With a partner, describe two ways in which the Interstate Highway system has changed the way things are done in the United States.

_____

_____

_____

_____

_____

Almanac Graph Practice

Highway Travel, 1960

Trip	Travel Time
Los Angeles–New York	51 hours
Dallas–Chicago	17 hours
Atlanta–Seattle	48 hours

Air Travel Today

Trip	Travel Time
Los Angeles–New York	5 hrs., 5 min.
Dallas–Chicago	2 hrs., 15 min.
Atlanta–Seattle	5 hrs., 30 min.

Practice

1. How long does it take to fly from Dallas to Chicago?

_____

2. How long did it take to travel from Los Angeles to New York by car in

1960? _____

Apply

3. Use the information below to complete the bar graph.

Top Five Cities Visited by Overseas Travelers in 2005

City	Number of Visitors
New York, NY	5,810,000
Los Angeles, CA	2,580,000
San Francisco, CA	2,124,000
Miami, FL	2,081,000
Orlando, FL	2,016,000

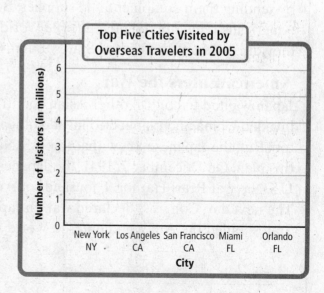

Top Five Cities Visited by Overseas Travelers in 2005

Summary: World War II

Start of the War

In the 1930s, the Great Depression ruined the economies of many nations. People wanted strong leaders to solve their problems. Dictators rose to power. In 1933, Adolf Hitler became Germany's dictator. Hitler belonged to a political party called the Nazis. They believed in fascism. Hitler also encouraged racism. He blamed the Jewish people for Germany's problems.

The leaders of Germany, Italy, and Japan encouraged nationalism. They attacked other countries. Joseph Stalin, the leader of the Soviet Union, and Hitler agreed not to attack each other. This allowed Hitler to attack other countries. Germany formed an alliance with Italy and Japan. These nations were called the Axis Powers.

Britain and France formed an alliance called the Allied Powers. They tried to stop Germany by signing an agreement with Hitler. The Allies would allow Hitler to keep the land his armies had already taken if Hitler stopped attacking other countries.

On September 1, 1939, Hitler broke his promise. Germany attacked Poland. The Allies declared war on Germany. Then Italy and Japan declared war on the Allies. By the end of 1941, Germany controlled all of Europe except Britain. The Germans bombed Britain many times. United States President Franklin D. Roosevelt helped the British by sending them equipment and supplies. Because most Americans remembered how terrible World War I had been, they did not want the United States to fight in Europe again.

America Enters the War

Japan wanted to control other Asian countries. Japan invaded China and planned to invade other Asian nations too. But, the Japanese knew that the U.S. Navy could stop this plan. On December 7, 1941, the Japanese attacked the U.S. Navy at Pearl Harbor. Thousands of Americans died. The next day, Congress declared war on Japan. The United States joined the Allies and entered World War II.

Before You Read

Find and underline each vocabulary word.

fascism *noun,* when a government controls its country's economy, culture, and people's lives

dictator *noun,* a ruler who has total control of a country and its people

racism *noun,* the idea that one race, or group of people, is better than other races

After You Read

REVIEW **How did the Allies try to stop Germany before September 1, 1939?** Underline the sentence that tells the answer.

REVIEW **Why did Congress declare war on Japan?** What happened at Pearl Harbor in 1941? Circle the sentence that tells the answer.

Practice Book
112   Use with *United States: Civil War to Today,* pp. 298–301

Reading Skill and Strategy

Reading Skill: Sequence

This skill helps you understand the order in which events happened.

Read "America Enters the War." Then fill in the sequence chart below to show the order in which the United States was brought into World War II.

1.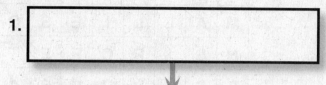

Americans were stunned by the attack and called for war.

2.

Reading Strategy: Monitor/Clarify

3. Read "Start of the War." Then check the statement that best clarifies the section.

____ A fascist government tells people what to do and how to think.

____ After conquering Poland, Germany attacked Italy.

____ The Axis Powers agreed to trade weapons with the Allies.

4. Read "Pearl Harbor." Then check the statement that best clarifies the section.

____ Most Americans believed in isolationism.

____ Japanese airplanes attacked Pearl Harbor, and Congress declared war on Japan.

____ Japan took over parts of China and had plans to invade other Asian nations.

113 Use with *United States: Civil War to Today*, pp. 298–301

Vocabulary and Study Guide

Vocabulary

Solve the clue and write the answer in the blank. Then find the word in the puzzle. Look up, down, forward, and backward. Look for a bonus word!

1. Adolf Hitler was this type of leader.

   _____

2. The idea that one race of people is better than

   others _____

3. When government controls the economy, culture,

   and people's lives _____

   Bonus Word:

T	R	O	B	U	Q	M	R
M	A	L	L	I	E	S	O
N	S	I	R	C	F	E	T
E	S	I	V	D	H	B	A
O	I	Z	C	G	E	U	T
A	S	J	S	S	M	R	C
K	M	S	I	C	A	R	I
O	P	I	N	S	R	F	D
L	G	N	A	F	D	O	E

Study Guide

4. Read "Start of the War." Then fill in the blanks below.

   The _____ ruined the economies of many

   nations around the world. In Germany, Adolf Hitler and the

   _____ Party took power. Hitler ruled as a

   _____. He built a powerful military. The leaders

   of _____ also encouraged feelings of nationalism.

   Germany, Italy, and Japan began attacking other countries. They

   formed an _____ called the Axis Powers.

5. Read "America Enters the War." Then fill in the blanks below.

   At the beginning of World War II, President Roosevelt

   sent supplies and _____ to Britain. He also

   worried about Japan's new nationalism. To try to keep the

   _____ from interfering, Japan made a surprise

   attack on the U.S. naval base in _____, Hawaii.

   The next day, _____ declared war on Japan.

Summary: The Home Front

Building an Army

The United States' military was unprepared for a big war in the 1920s and 1930s. When Japan attacked Pearl Harbor in 1941, the United States needed to mobilize for war. Americans joined the armed forces and were drafted. The soldiers needed guns, uniforms, airplanes, and tanks. More than 15 million Americans joined the armed forces, including 100,000 women.

The government paid businesses hundreds of billions of dollars to make supplies. Factories hired millions of new workers. Many of them were African Americans and women. Some factories stopped making consumer goods to make military supplies. U.S. factories made more war supplies than the other nations. American scientists made better helicopters and airplanes. Scientists also developed radar. Radar was used to find airplanes and ships that were far away.

At Home in Wartime

Many Americans helped support the war. Groups collected supplies for soldiers. Children collected metal and old tires. Factories used them to make supplies. The military also needed lots of food for the soldiers. Meat, sugar, and gasoline were rationed. Many families planted victory gardens to grow their own food. American culture changed. Many people knew someone fighting in the war. Newsreels told about the war. People wrote books, plays, movies, and songs about the war.

Many people were afraid Japanese Americans would help Japan during the war. The government forced over 100,000 Japanese Americans to move to internment camps. Some Italian Americans and German Americans were sent to internment camps. Most of these people were American citizens. Thousands of Japanese Americans fought for the United States.

✏ Before You Read

Find and underline each vocabulary word.

mobilize *verb,* to get ready to fight

newsreel *noun,* a short film about current events

internment camp *noun,* a place where prisoners are held during wartime

✏ After You Read

REVIEW **Why did the United States have to produce so many military supplies?** What were the United States' armed forces like in the 1920s and 1930s? What was the U.S. military like when Japan attacked Pearl Harbor in 1941? Underline the two sentences that tell you the answer.

REVIEW **What did Americans at home do to help the war effort?** Highlight three ways that Americans helped the war effort.

Use with *United States: Civil War to Today,* pp. 302–305

Reading Skill and Strategy

Reading Skill: Problem and Solution

This skill helps you see what problem some people faced and how they resolved it.

Read "The Home Front." Then fill in the problem-and-solution chart below. How did the United States prepare for war?

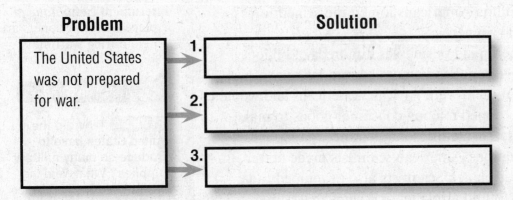

Problem   **Solution**

The United States was not prepared for war.

1.

2.

3.

Reading Strategy: Monitor/Clarify

4. Read "Building an Army." Then check the statement that best clarifies the section.

   ____ Americans joined the army and made supplies for the military.

   ____ Japan built more airplanes than any other country in World War II.

   ____ During the war, women were not allowed to join the armed forces.

5. Read "At Home in Wartime." Then complete the statements.

   Because the armed forces needed supplies, goods such

   as _____ were rationed. Also,

   _____ built airplane engines

   instead of cars to help the war effort.

Vocabulary and Study Guide

Vocabulary

1. Draw a line connecting the vocabulary word to its meaning.

newsreel	to get ready to fight
mobilize	a place where prisoners are held during wartime
internment camp	a short film about current events

Study Guide

Read "Building an Army." Then fill in the main-idea-and-details chart below.

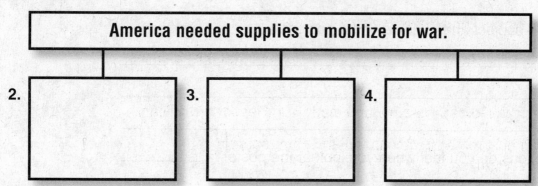

America needed supplies to mobilize for war.

2.

3.

4.

Read "At Home in Wartime." Then answer the questions.

5. Name two effects World War II had on American life.

_____

_____

_____

6. Why were more than 100,000 Japanese Americans sent to internment camps?

_____

_____

Use with *United States: Civil War to Today*, pp. 302–305

Skillbuilder: Recognize Propaganda

During World War II, United States citizens were asked to pull together to help the war effort. Posters reminded people of things they could do, and why it was important. Look at the poster below and answer the questions.

Practice

1. What is the subject and purpose of the poster? _____

_____

_____

_____

2. What emotions do you feel when you look at the poster? _____

_____

3. Does the poster have a bias and propaganda? Explain your answer.

_____

_____

_____

_____

Apply

Read "At Home in Wartime" in Lesson 2. Make your own World War II poster encouraging the efforts of people at home. Explain to the class how your poster shows some bias.

Summary: Ending the War

Battles in North Africa and Europe

German and Japanese victories surprised the Allies at first. In late 1942, they fought back. The Allies defeated Germans and Italians in North Africa. Then the Allies attacked Italy. At the same time, the Soviets defeated German troops. Allied airplanes took control of the skies over Europe.

On June 6, 1944, nearly 200,000 Allied soldiers invaded France. This is known as D-day. One million soldiers landed in France within 10 days. The Allies and Soviet soldiers advanced on Germany. Germany surrendered in May, 1945. This day was called Victory in Europe Day, or V-E Day.

Fighting in the Pacific

Japan still held parts of the western Pacific and eastern Asia. In June 1942, the Allies won the Battle of Midway. Allied planes shot down Japanese planes. They sank Japanese aircraft carriers. America won more power in the Pacific. However, the Japanese still held islands there. The Allies skipped over some Japanese islands and captured others. They used the captured islands to attack islands closer to Japan. Navajo Indian code talkers used a secret code to send messages to Allied leaders. The Japanese could not understand the messages.

On August 6, 1945, Americans dropped an atomic bomb on Hiroshima, Japan. It killed nearly 100,000 people. Three days later, the United States dropped an atomic bomb on Nagasaki. Japan surrendered. August 14, 1945, was called Victory in Japan Day. It is known as V-J Day.

A Changed World

Millions of people died during the war. Many people lost their homes and had no food. Cities were ruined. After the fighting ended, Allied soldiers discovered that the Nazis had killed millions of people in concentration camps. About twelve million people died or were killed in concentration camps. About six million were Jews. This mass murder is called the Holocaust.

Before You Read

Find and underline each vocabulary word.

aircraft carrier *noun*, a large ship that carries airplanes far from land

atomic bomb *noun*, a powerful bomb that can destroy an entire city

concentration camp *noun*, a place where large numbers of people are held prisoner and forced to work

After You Read

REVIEW **Why was D-day important?** What did Allied soldiers do on D-day? Circle the sentence that tells you the answer. What did it allow the Allies to do? Draw a box around the sentence that tells you the answer.

REVIEW **Why was the Battle of Midway important?** What did America win? Circle the answer.

REVIEW **What was the Holocaust?** What did Nazis do in concentration camps? Highlight the sentences that tell the answer.

Practice Book
119
Use with *United States: Civil War to Today*, pp. 310–315

Reading Skill and Strategy

Reading Skill: Cause and Effect

This skill helps you see how one event can be related to another, either by causing it or resulting from it.

Read "Winning the War." Then fill in the cause-and-effect chart below. What were two effects of the Allies striking back against the Axis?

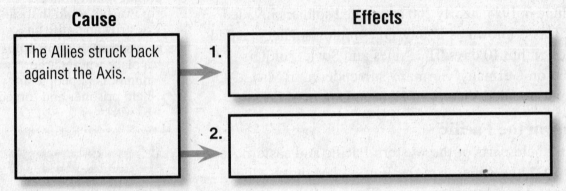

Cause

The Allies struck back against the Axis.

Effects

1.

2.

Reading Strategy: Monitor/Clarify

3. Read "Battles in North Africa and Europe." Then complete the statement.

   Germany surrendered after it was invaded by the Allies from

   the west and _____.

4. Read "Fighting in the Pacific." Then explain why Navajo code talkers were so important to the war in the Pacific.

   _____

   _____

   _____

Vocabulary and Study Guide

Vocabulary

If you do not know a word's meaning, try breaking it into smaller parts. It may contain a smaller word that you know.

Find the smaller words inside these words. Use what you know about the smaller word or words to write the meaning of the longer word.

	New word	Words in it that I know	Word meanings that I know	What I think the word means
1.	aircraft carrier			
2.	atomic bomb			
3.	concentration camp			

Study Guide

Read "Ending the War." Then fill in the chart and answer the questions below.

Event	What happened
D-day	4.
V-E Day	5.
V-J Day	6.

7. Name two military strategies the Allies used in the Pacific.

_____

8. What did President Truman do instead of invading Japan? Why?

_____

_____

9. What happened in concentration camps during World War II? _____

_____

Use with *United States: Civil War to Today*, pp. 310–315

Summary: The Cold War

Roots of the Cold War

The United States and the Soviet Union worked together to win World War II. Differences between the countries pushed them apart after the war. The countries had different ideas about economics and government. Americans live under capitalism. They have a market economy. Americans have a democratic government. They vote for their leaders. Soviets lived under communism. They did not choose their leaders. Soviets did not have much freedom.

By 1947, the Soviet Union and the United States were in a Cold War. This was a war of words and ideas. When World War II ended, the Allies shared control of Germany. The Soviet Union controlled the eastern half. The United States, Britain, and France controlled the western half. The capital city of Berlin was divided. The Soviets controlled East Berlin. The Allies controlled West Berlin.

The Soviet Union created communist governments in Eastern Europe. Winston Churchill said an "iron curtain" divided Europe. The curtain was not real. It was a symbol of the differences between communist and noncommunist countries. In 1949, the United States, Canada, Britain, and most of the noncommunist European countries formed the North Atlantic Treaty Organization, or NATO. It wanted to keep the Soviets from forcing communism on other nations.

Conflicts in Europe Grow

Soviets blocked the roads and railroads to West Berlin in 1948. The United States and Britain broke this blockade. Airplanes took food and supplies to people trapped in West Berlin. This was called the Berlin Airlift. Many people from East Berlin escaped to West Berlin during the 1950s. In 1961, the Soviets began to build a wall. It divided East Berlin and West Berlin. It was called the Berlin Wall.

Before You Read

Find and underline each vocabulary word.

capitalism *noun,* when ordinary people and businesses control the production of goods and services

market economy *noun,* when individuals and businesses make most economic decisions

communism *noun,* when a government controls production and owns the nation's natural and capital resources

After You Read

REVIEW **What area did the Soviet Union take control of after World War II?** Circle the sentence that tells which half of Germany the Soviet Union controlled. Then underline the sentence that tells which countries controlled the other half.

REVIEW **How did the United States and Britain help end the blockade of Berlin?** How did the United States and Britain help the people trapped in West Berlin? Circle the sentence that tells you the answer.

Practice Book
122
Use with *United States: Civil War to Today,* pp. 318–321

Reading Skill and Strategy

Reading Skill: Compare and Contrast

This skill helps you understand how historical events or people are similar and different.

Read "The Cold War." Then fill in the compare-and-contrast chart below to compare and contrast the Soviet Union and the United States.

Soviet Union	United States
• Communist government • People had no control over the government • Citizens had few rights and little freedom	1. 2. 3.

Reading Strategy: Monitor/Clarify

4. Read "Roots of the Cold War." Then complete the statement.

   In a _____, the government controls

   production and owns the nation's natural and capital resources.

5. Read "Roots of the Cold War." Then explain why Winston Churchill said that Europe was divided by "an iron curtain."

   _____

   _____

6. Read "Conflicts in Europe Grow." Then explain why Soviet leaders built the Berlin Wall.

   _____

   _____

Vocabulary and Study Guide

Vocabulary

As you read the chapter, fill in the chart below with words from the box.

capitalism	communism	market economy

Government controls production	People and businesses control production
1. _____ _____	2. _____ _____

Study Guide

3. Read "Roots of the Cold War." Then fill in the blanks below.

   The _____ began in Europe as World War II came

   to an end. The Soviet Union set up _____ governments

   in much of Eastern Europe while Western Europe stayed

   _____. The idea of the _____ symbolized

   the differences that divided communist and noncommunist

   nations. To help stop the spread of communism,

   noncommunist countries formed an alliance called

   _____.

Read "Conflicts in Europe Grow." Then choose the correct ending to each statement below.

4. The Soviet Union tried to take control of Berlin by creating

   A. an invasion. **B.** a treaty. **C.** a blockade.

5. The Berlin Airlift was an action taken by the United States and

   A. France. **B.** Britain. **C.** NATO.

6. The Soviets built the Berlin Wall to keep the people of East Berlin from

   A. receiving goods. **B.** escaping. **C.** traveling.

Summary: Arms Race

Communism Around the World

After World War II, Americans worried that Soviets would spread communism everywhere. The Soviets helped a communist army in China. China became communist. Now two of the biggest nations in the world were communist.

In 1949, the Soviet Union built an atomic bomb. U.S. leaders wanted their military to be stronger than the Soviets'. An arms race began. People worried this race would lead to a nuclear war. During the 1950s, anti-communism grew in the United States. Joseph McCarthy was an anti-communist who claimed that communists worked in the U.S. government. Anti-communists in Congress searched for communists. Hundreds of government workers were fired. A few spies were found. Most people were innocent, though.

Cold War Conflicts

After World War II, the Allies formed the United Nations (UN). More than 50 countries joined the UN to try to keep peace in the world.

In 1950, North Korea was communist. South Korea was not. North Korea invaded South Korea. The Soviets supported North Korea. The United States convinced the UN to defend South Korea. UN soldiers pushed North Koreans out of South Korea. Then China began to help North Korea. In 1953, the two sides agreed to stop fighting. Neither side won.

In 1959, Fidel Castro led a revolution in Cuba, an island near the United States. The Soviets helped Castro set up a communist government in Cuba. In 1962, the United States learned that Soviets were shipping missiles to Cuba. The missiles could carry atomic bombs. President John F. Kennedy sent U.S. ships to block Cuba. This was called the Cuban missile crisis. People feared it would lead to a nuclear war. Days later, Soviets removed the missiles. The United States promised not to attack Cuba. The Soviet Union and the United States agreed to try to prevent nuclear war together.

Before You Read

Find and underline each vocabulary word.

arms race *noun,* a race between nations to build more powerful weapons

nuclear war *noun,* a war in which powerful nuclear weapons are used

anti-communism *noun,* a movement to stop the spread of communism and communist ideas

After You Read

REVIEW **Who was Joseph McCarthy?** Highlight the sentence that tells the answer.

REVIEW **What did President Kennedy do to end the Cuban missile crisis?** What did President Kennedy send to block Cuba? Underline the sentence that tells the answer.

Use with *United States: Civil War to Today,* pp. 324–327

Reading Skill and Strategy

Reading Skill: Draw Conclusions

Sometimes when you read, you have to figure out things that the writer doesn't tell you. This skill is called drawing conclusions.

Read "Nuclear War." Then fill in the draw conclusions chart below. How was the Soviet Union different from the United States?

Detail	**Detail**
The United States developed nuclear weapons.	The Soviet Union also tried to make nuclear weapons.

1. **Conclusion**

Reading Strategy: Monitor/Clarify

2. Read "Cold War Conflicts." Then tell how you monitored your understanding of the section.

_____

_____

3. Write a question you had after you finished reading.

_____

_____

4. How did you answer your question? Answer with a complete sentence.

_____

_____

Practice Book
126
Use with *United States: Civil War to Today*, pp. 324–327

Vocabulary and Study Guide

Vocabulary

Write the definition of each vocabulary word below.

1. arms race _____

_____

2. nuclear war _____

_____

3. anti-communism _____

_____

4. Use two of the words in a sentence. _____

_____

Study Guide

Read "Communism Around the World." Then fill in the chart below.

Causes	Effect
5.	The fear of communism increased in the United States.
6.	
7.	

8. Read "Cold War Conflicts." Then fill in the blanks below.

When troops from Communist _____

invaded South Korea, the United States thought that the

_____ had helped plan the attack.

The United Nations sent in forces to defend South Korea.

After years of fierce fighting, neither side won.

Use with *United States: Civil War to Today*, pp. 324–327

Summary: Growth and Prosperity

Government in the 1950s

After World War II, millions of soldiers returned to the United States. They needed jobs and homes. President Harry Truman wanted the government to help. He created the Fair Deal in 1949. It included laws to create jobs and build houses. The laws tried to help African Americans get equal treatment when they voted and applied for jobs. Congress did not pass many of the laws. Many Americans thought people didn't need the government's help.

In 1952, General Dwight D. Eisenhower was elected President. He was very popular because he was a war hero who had led the Allied troops in Europe during World War II. As President he helped end the Korean War in 1953. People liked his warm personality. President Eisenhower approved the Federal-Aid Highway Act in 1956, which gave over $32 billion to build modern highways. He thought new roads would make it easier to move people and goods around the country. Under Eisenhower's leadership the economy grew. He ran for re-election in 1956, using the slogan "peace, progress and prosperity."

Americans at Home

When veterans went back to work they were eager to buy houses and start families. So many new families were started in the 1950s that the country had a baby boom. There were not enough houses. Builders bought land outside of the cities and built large housing projects. The projects had houses that looked alike and were built very close together. The government lent money to help millions of veterans buy these houses.

The economy grew fast. More people had money to spend. They bought cars and household appliances, such as washing machines, vacuum cleaners, and televisions. Television brought news from far away right into their homes. Factories and businesses worked faster to make more products. Medicine also improved. In 1956, Dr. Jonas Salk invented a vaccine to prevent people from getting polio.

Before You Read

Find and underline each vocabulary word.

prosperity *noun*, economic success, such as earning a good income

veteran *noun*, a person who has served in the military

baby boom *noun*, the increase in the number of babies born after World War II

vaccine *noun*, a medicine to protect people against a disease

After You Read

REVIEW What made President Eisenhower so popular? Underline three sentences that tell why Americans liked Eisenhower.

REVIEW What was the effect of the baby boom on home building? Circle the sentence that describes the housing problem in the 1950s. Then draw a box around the sentences that tell the solution.

Reading Skill and Strategy

Reading Skill: Sequence

This skill helps you understand the order in which events happened.

Read "Government in the 1950s." Then fill in the sequence chart below to show the order of events in government in the 1950s.

	Eisenhower became President.
1.	
2.	
3.	

Reading Strategy: Question

4. Read "Government in the 1950s." Then check the question that you might ask while reading this section.

_____ How many miles of modern highways were built as a result of the Federal-Aid Highway Act?

_____ How did Truman's Fair Deal try to help African Americans?

_____ Who was elected President in 1956?

5. Read "Americans at Home." Then check the question that you might ask while reading this section.

_____ How many station wagons were produced during the baby boom of the 1950s?

_____ What were the most popular radio programs in the 1950s?

_____ What did the government do to help veterans buy homes?

Vocabulary and Study Guide

Vocabulary

Across

1. Used to prevent polio

3. Eisenhower's campaign slogan was "peace, progress and _____."

Down

1. A person who has served in the military

2. The increase in the number of babies born in the United States after World War II

Study Guide

4. Read "Government in the 1950s." Then fill in the blanks below.

President Truman worked hard to convince Congress to pass

his _____ laws. He proposed laws to build houses, help

African Americans, and _____. However, many Americans

did not think people needed help from the _____.

President _____ was a war hero. Under his leadership,

transportation improved, and the U.S. _____ grew rapidly.

5. Read "Americans at Home." Then fill in the blanks below.

The return of the _____ from World War II caused

a big boost in the U.S. economy. Many people started families.

The _____ created a housing shortage, and many

housing projects were built in the _____. People bought

record numbers of _____ and other household items.

_____ improved and became less expensive to own. Dr.

Jonas Salk developed a vaccine to prevent _____.

Practice Book

130

Use with *United States: Civil War to Today*, pp. 334–337

Summary: Civil Rights

The Movement Begins

The end of slavery was not the end of inequality. African Americans were denied the civil rights guaranteed by the Constitution. In the early 1950s, many public places were segregated. People were separated by race. Many Americans thought segregation was wrong. They wanted desegregation. In 1954, the Supreme Court said segregation of public schools was illegal because African American children did not get an equal education. In Montgomery, Alabama, buses were segregated. In 1955, Rosa Parks, an African American woman, sat in the white section of a bus. The Montgomery Bus Boycott began. Protesters stopped riding buses. Martin Luther King Jr. led nonviolent protests. In 1956, bus segregation became illegal.

Civil Rights Victories

In 1960, African Americans in 54 cities held protests called "sit-ins." They sat in segregated restaurants until they were served. Freedom Riders tested desegregation in the South. They used public places that were once for "whites only." People who were against desegregation attacked them. Martin Luther King Jr. organized a children's protest. The police attacked the protesters. In Washington, D.C., King organized a march and gave his famous "I have a dream" speech.

Gains and Losses

In the 1960s, religious and ethnic groups, including women and Native Americans, fought for civil rights. Cesar Chavez and Dolores Huerta organized farm workers to improve work conditions. The Civil Rights Act of 1964 made segregation illegal in schools, workplaces, and public places. Change was slow. Laws made it difficult for African Americans to vote. In 1965, the Voting Rights Act made it illegal to stop people from voting because of their race. In 1968, Martin Luther King, Jr., was assassinated. This did not stop the civil rights movement. People from many backgrounds joined the struggle for civil rights.

Before You Read

Find and underline each vocabulary word.

civil rights *noun*, rights that countries guarantee their citizens

desegregation *noun*, ending the separation of people by racial or ethnic group

nonviolent protest *noun*, a way of bringing change without using violence

After You Read

REVIEW **What was the goal of the Montgomery Bus Boycott?** Circle the sentence that tells what happened because African Americans stopped riding buses in Montgomery, Alabama.

REVIEW **What was the purpose of the restaurant sit-ins?** Circle the sentence that tells what happened because of the sit-ins.

REVIEW **What did the Civil Rights Act do?** Circle the sentence that tells what the Civil Rights Act did.

Use with *United States: Civil War to Today*, pp. 340–345

Reading Skill and Strategy

Reading Skill: Cause and Effect

This skill helps you see how one event can be related to another, either by causing it or resulting from it.

Read "Civil Rights." Then fill in the cause-and-effects chart below to show two effects of desegregation in the South.

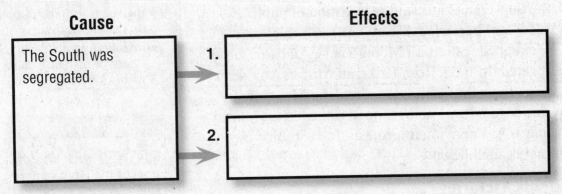

Cause

The South was segregated.

Effects

1.

2.

Reading Strategy: Question

3. Read "The Movement Begins." Then check the question that you might ask while reading this section.

_____ How was the right to vote guaranteed for African Americans?

_____ What was the result of the Supreme Court's decision in Linda Brown's case?

_____ What was boycotted in Montgomery, Alabama, besides buses?

4. Read "Civil Rights Victories." Read the question. Then complete the answer to the question.

   Question: How many people participated in the March on Washington, and why?

   Answer: More than 200,000 people marched in Washington, D.C., to _____.

Practice Book
132   Use with *United States: Civil War to Today*, pp. 340–345

Vocabulary and Study Guide

Vocabulary

1. Draw a line connecting the vocabulary word to its meaning.

desegregation	the rights that countries guarantee their citizens
civil rights	a way to bring change without using violence
nonviolent protest	ending the separation of people by racial or ethnic group

Study Guide

Read "The Movement Begins." Then describe what the people in the chart below did to help end segregation.

Linda Brown's parents	Rosa Parks	Martin Luther King Jr.
2.	3.	4.

Read "Civil Rights Victories." Then answer the questions below.

5. What did the Freedom Riders do? Why?

_____

_____

_____

6. What did Martin Luther King Jr. do at the 1963 March on Washington?

_____

_____

_____

133   Use with *United States: Civil War to Today*, pp. 340–345

Summary: Time of Change

Kennedy and Johnson

John F. Kennedy was the youngest United States President ever elected. He believed people, including young people, could make the world better. He started a program called the New Frontier to make life in the United States better. He also started the Peace Corps to help people in other countries.

The United States and the Soviet Union were in a space race to see which country could send people into outer space. In 1957, the Soviet Union sent *Sputnik I* around the earth. *Sputnik I* was the first object made by people ever to circle Earth.

In 1961, the Soviets sent the first person, Yuri Gagarin, into space to orbit Earth. The United States hurried to do the same. A month after Gagarin, Alan Shepard was the first American in space. In 1962, John Glenn became the first American to go around Earth. Seven years later, Americans Neil Armstrong and Buzz Aldrin became the first people to land on the moon.

President Kennedy never saw the moon landing because he was assassinated in 1963. Americans were shocked and sad. Vice President Lyndon Johnson became President. He also believed the government should help people. He started a program called the "Great Society" to help people in need. He said there should be a "war on poverty." The welfare system was started to help give food, housing, medical care, and education to people who needed them. It also trained people for jobs.

A Changing Culture

In the 1960s, the baby boom generation became teenagers. They liked a new kind of music called rock 'n' roll, sung by American and British bands. In the 1950s, musicians like Elvis Presley and Chuck Berry helped create this new music. In the 1960s, teenagers listened to American groups such as the *Beach Boys* and the *Supremes*. The British band the *Beatles* became famous. Artists and sculptors made "pop art" with colorful designs. Artists made fun of American's interest in television, magazines, advertising, and buying things. The baby boom generation wanted to change the world.

Before You Read

Find and underline each vocabulary word.

space race *noun,* a competition between the United States and the Soviet Union to send people into outer space

welfare *noun,* a government program that helps people who are in need

generation *noun,* a group of people born and living at about the same time

After You Read

REVIEW Who was the first person to orbit Earth? Circle the name of the person.

REVIEW What kind of music was most popular with teenagers during the 1960s? Circle the words that tell what kind of music was most popular in the 1960s.

Practice Book
134 Use with *United States: Civil War to Today,* pp. 348–351

Reading Skill and Strategy

Reading Skill: Main Idea and Details

This skill helps you understand events by seeing how they are related.

Read "The Space Race." Then fill in the chart below.

> The United States and the Soviet Union competed to send people into outer space.

> 1.

> 2.

Reading Strategy: Question

3. Read "Kennedy and Johnson." Read the answer. Then complete the question for the answer.

   Answer: Sputnik I

   What was the name of _____

   _____?

4. Read "A Changing Culture." Then write a question and the answer to it.

   Question: _____

   _____

   Answer: _____

   _____

Vocabulary and Study Guide

Vocabulary

Write the definition of each vocabulary word below.

1. space race _____

_____

2. welfare _____

_____

3. generation _____

_____

4. Use two of the words in a sentence. _____

_____

Study Guide

Read "Kennedy and Johnson." Then fill in the chart below.

President Kennedy's programs	President Johnson's programs
5.	6.

Read "A Changing Culture." Then fill in the chart below.

Baby boom children changed American culture.

Rock 'n' roll became the most popular music for young people.	7.	8.

Use with *United States: Civil War to Today*, pp. 348–351

Skillbuilder: Analyze the News

Major Victory in the Space Race!

For years the United States and the Soviet Union have competed to send people into outer space. The Soviet Union had some minor success by sending a rocket, *Sputnik I*, into outer space in 1957, and in 1961, Soviet cosmonaut Yuri Gagarin was able to orbit Earth in a space capsule. Not to be outdone, the United States matched this feat a year later when John Glenn orbited Earth. Yesterday, however, on July 20, 1969, the United States won a major victory in the space race by landing two men on the moon. Entering outer space at all was an accomplishment for both nations, but traveling to and setting foot upon another world has clearly put the United States in the lead in this race.

Practice

1. Is this a news article or an editorial? Why? _____

_____

_____

2. What are two facts that are given? _____

_____

_____

3. What are two opinions that are given? _____

_____

4. How would you describe the writer's point of view? _____

_____

Apply

Read about President Johnson's war on poverty in "Johnson Becomes President." Then write a short editorial in support of Great Society programs.

Summary: The Vietnam War

The Conflict in Vietnam

During the 1950s and 1960s, the United States fought wars to stop communism. Vietnam had been a French colony since the 1880s. The Vietnamese fought for independence and won in 1954. The country was split into communist North Vietnam and non-communist South Vietnam.

Communists in South Vietnam were called the Vietcong. In the early 1960s, they tried to overthrow the government. North Vietnam helped the Vietcong. The United States sent military advisers and supplies to help South Vietnam fight the Vietcong.

In 1965, the U.S. sent soldiers to Vietnam. The U.S. troops had better technology and weapons. They had jet bombers, tanks, and helicopters. The Vietcong fought in small groups that hid in the jungle. They controlled most of South Vietnam.

The Antiwar Movement

The U.S. was spending billions of dollars on the war. Many American soldiers were dying. On television people saw soldiers fighting dangerous battles and the terrible results of U.S. bombs on Vietnamese people. Some people thought the United States had to fight communism everywhere. Others thought the United States should stay out of a war between North and South Vietnam.

The government drafted young men into the army. Many did not want to fight in a war they believed was wrong. People had antiwar demonstrations in many parts of the country.

In 1969, Richard Nixon was elected President. He started bringing soldiers home. But U.S. planes also increased bombing of North Vietnam and started bombing Cambodia, a country west of Vietnam. In 1973, North Vietnam, South Vietnam, and the United States agreed to a cease-fire. U.S. soldiers went home. The North Vietnamese won the war in 1975. Over 55,000 Americans died in the war. Communism was not stopped in Vietnam.

Before You Read

Find and underline each vocabulary word.

overthrow *verb*, to remove from power

demonstration *noun*, a gathering of people who want to express their opinions to the public and to the government

cease-fire *noun*, an agreement to stop all fighting

After You Read

REVIEW What did the Vietcong do to fight against the technology of the United States military? Circle the sentence that tells how the Vietcong fought the war.

REVIEW Why did many people in the United States protest against the war in Vietnam? Highlight sentences that tell what people in America learned and saw on television as the war continued. Circle the sentence that tells why people protested against the war.

Reading Skill and Strategy

Reading Skill: Compare and Contrast

This skill helps you understand how historical events or people are similar and different.

Read "The Conflict in Vietnam." Then fill in the compare-and-contrast chart below to compare and contrast United States soldiers and the Vietcong.

United States soldiers	Vietcong
They had better technology.	1.
They had helicopters, tanks, and weapons.	2.
They were not used to fighting in the jungle.	3.

Reading Strategy: Question

Look over "The Vietnam War." Read the headings. Then turn each heading into a question. As you read, look for the answers to those questions.

4. Heading 1: The Conflict in Vietnam

   Question: _____
   _____

   Answer: _____
   _____
   _____

5. Heading 2: The Antiwar Movement

   Question: _____
   _____

   Answer: _____
   _____
   _____

Use with *United States: Civil War to Today*, pp. 358–361

Vocabulary and Study Guide

Vocabulary

If you do not know a word's meaning, try breaking it into smaller parts. It may contain a smaller word that you know.

Find the smaller words inside these words. Use what you know about the smaller word or words to write the meaning of the longer word.

	New word	Words in it that I know	Word meanings that I know	What I think the word means
1.	overthrow			
2.	cease-fire			

3. Use *demonstration* in a sentence about the Vietnam War.

_____

_____

Study Guide

4. Read "The Conflict in Vietnam." Then fill in the blanks below.

In the early 1960s, communist fighters called Vietcong

began trying to _____ the government of

_____. The United States sent supplies, advisers,

and _____ to help South Vietnam fight communism.

The fighting increased when the _____ army

joined the Vietcong. Even though the United States had advanced

_____ on its side, the fast-moving Vietcong soldiers

controlled most of South Vietnam.

Almanac Map Practice

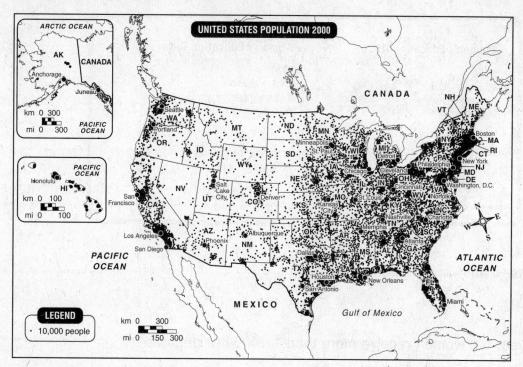

Use the map to do these activities and answer these questions.

Practice

1. How many people does one dot on the map represent? _____

2. Name the two cities in California whose populations seem to border
   each other. _____

3. In which region of the United States does the population seem the
   most dense or compressed? _____

4. Which state seems more densely populated, Alaska or Hawaii? How
   can you tell? _____

   _____

Apply

5. With a partner, study the "Electoral Votes" map on page 397 of
   Chapter 11. How does the number of electoral votes in California and
   Nevada relate to each state's population?

   _____

   _____

Practice Book

141   Use with *United States: Civil War to Today*, pp. 370–371

Name _____ Date _____

Almanac Graph Practice

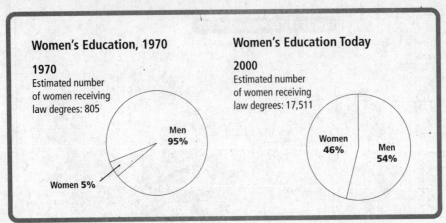

Women's Education, 1970

1970
Estimated number
of women receiving
law degrees: 805

Men
95%

Women 5%

Women's Education Today

2000
Estimated number
of women receiving
law degrees: 17,511

Women
46%

Men
54%

Use the graphs to answer these questions.

Practice

1. In which year did women receive more than 17,000 law degrees?

_____

2. How much greater was the percentage of degrees received by

women in 2000 than in 1970? _____

Apply

3. Complete the circle graphs using the information below. Draw lines to
make sections in each circle. Write the terms *college* or *no college* in
each section.

In 1947, 4.7% of all women in the United States went to college for
four or more years. In 2003, 25.7% of all women in the United States
went to college for four or more years.

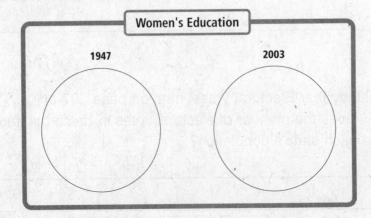

Women's Education

1947

2003

Summary: Elections, the Economy, and Equality

The Nixon Years

Richard Nixon was elected President in 1968. He helped build better relations between the United States and the two countries, China and the Soviet Union.

In 1973, Israel was attacked by Egypt and Syria. Oil-producing countries that supported Egypt and Syria wanted to punish the United States for helping Israel. They produced less oil, so oil prices went up. High oil prices made costs rise for making and shipping goods, so prices rose. This is called inflation.

In 1972, Nixon's campaign workers broke into the Democratic Party headquarters in the Watergate building to steal information. They were caught. Nixon said he did not know about the break-in. An investigation proved that he had lied and was trying to cover up the crime. Nixon had to resign in 1974. Vice President Gerald Ford became President.

A Time of Change

In the 1970s, many people struggled for equal rights. Women were paid less than men for doing the same job. They wanted equality. By the late 1980s, more women were legislators and 40 states had equal pay laws.

American Indians on reservations did not have good health care or education. Unemployment was high. They wanted help solving problems. They wanted the government to honor treaties. The migrant workers movement forced some employers to improve conditions. Consumers pushed for laws to improve product quality and product safety.

The Carter Years

In 1976, Jimmy Carter was elected President. Carter brought leaders from Israel and Egypt together to sign the Camp David Peace Accord. Carter tried to control inflation by raising taxes and lowering government spending. It did not work. In 1979, armed Iranian students took 52 American hostages. Although Carter worked for their release, he was unable to quickly free them. They were held for 444 days. In 1980, Carter lost the election to Ronald Reagan.

Before You Read

Find and underline each vocabulary word.

resign *verb*, to give up your job

migrant worker *noun*, a person who moves from place to place to find work, mostly on farms

accord *noun*, an agreement

After You Read

REVIEW **Which events caused inflation during the 1970s?** Highlight the sentence that tells what started the war in the Middle East in 1973. Then circle the sentences that tell what action oil-producing countries took.

REVIEW **What were two goals of the Indian rights movement?** Circle two sentences that tell you the answer.

REVIEW **What were President Jimmy Carter's successes and failures?** Highlight the sentence that tells what President Carter did to solve the problems in the Middle East. Draw a box around the sentences that tell his failures.

Use with *United States: Civil War to Today*, pp. 374–379

Reading Skill and Strategy

Reading Skill: Sequence

This skill helps you understand the order in which events happened.

Read "The Nixon Years." Then fill in the sequence chart below to show the order of events that led to Nixon's resignation.

1.	
2.	
3.	

Reading Strategy: Monitor/Clarify

4. Read "The Nixon Years." Then check the statement that best clarifies the section.

_____ Nixon improved the United States' relations with China and the Soviet Union.

_____ Israel attacked Egypt and Syria so they could sell more oil.

_____ Nixon resigned as President because of the high oil prices.

5. Read "The Carter Years." Then check the statement that best clarifies the section.

_____ President Carter was successful in fixing problems in the Middle East but struggled with inflation at home.

_____ Israel and Syria made peace by signing the Camp David Accord.

_____ Jimmy Carter was awarded the Nobel Peace Prize in 2002.

Vocabulary and Study Guide

Vocabulary

Write the definition of each vocabulary word below.

1. resign _____

2. accord _____

3. migrant worker _____

_____

Study Guide

Read "The Nixon Years" and "The Carter Years." Then fill in the compare-and-contrast chart below.

President	Successes	Problems
Richard Nixon	**4.**	**6.**
Jimmy Carter	**5.**	**7.**

Read "A Time of Change." Then fill in the category chart below to show the changes that came from each movement.

Women's rights movement	Migrant workers' rights movement	Consumers' rights movement
8.	**9.**	**10.**

Use with *United States: Civil War to Today,* pp. 374–379

Summary: Impact of the 1980s

Reagan Becomes President

Ronald Reagan was elected President in 1980. Many Presidents before Reagan used government money to pay for programs to provide people with services such as health care, job training, and housing. Reagan spent less money on government programs.

Reagan believed a strong economy would help people more than government programs. He used deregulation to help businesses. At the end of his term, about 20 million more people had jobs than when he took office. Reagan spent a lot more government money on the military. He thought a strong military would keep America safe and end the Cold War. Increased spending caused the highest deficit America had ever had.

International Events

In the 1980s, the Soviet Union was having serious trouble. Its economy could not provide enough goods, jobs, and housing for its people. Too much money was spent on the arms race with the United States.

Soviet leader Mikhail Gorbachev worked to end the Cold War. He wanted a better relationship with the United States. Reagan and Gorbachev first met in 1985 to talk about the arms race. In 1987, they signed a treaty that lowered the number of nuclear weapons each country had.

In 1988, George Bush was elected President. The Soviet Union was growing weaker. The Cold War was over. Many nations split from the Soviet Union to form independent countries.

In 1990, there was more trouble in the Middle East. Saddam Hussein, the leader of Iraq, invaded a neighboring country, Kuwait, to take over its oil fields. President Bush asked other countries in the United Nations to form a coalition to fight Iraq. The Persian Gulf War lasted about seven weeks. In 1991, the coalition forces won because they used advanced weapons and highly trained soldiers. Iraq left Kuwait, but Hussein stayed in power.

Before You Read

Find and underline each vocabulary word.

deregulation *noun,* the process of removing rules about what businesses can and cannot do

deficit *noun,* shortage caused by a government spending more money than it collects in taxes

coalition *noun,* a group of allies that work together to achieve a goal

After You Read

REVIEW Why did President Reagan spend government money on the military? Underline the sentence that tells the answer.

REVIEW How did President Reagan help end the Cold War? Highlight the sentence that tells who Reagan met with to talk about the arms race. Then circle the sentence that tells what the two leaders did.

Reading Skill and Strategy

Reading Skill: Main Idea and Details

This skill helps you understand events by seeing how they are related.

Read "The Persian Gulf War." Then fill in the main idea and details chart below. Write the main idea in the large box. Write details that support the main idea in the smaller boxes.

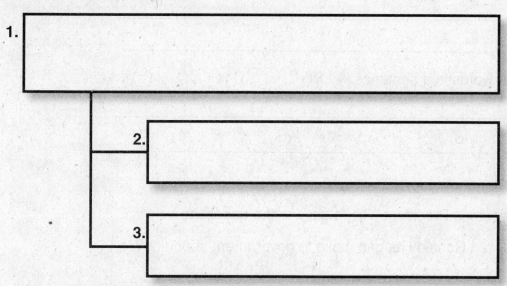

1.

2.

3.

Reading Strategy: Monitor/Clarify

4. Read "Reagan Becomes President." Then check the statement that best clarifies the section.

_____ Reagan spent government money to build a stronger military.

_____ Reagan raised taxes to pay for the stronger armed forces.

_____ Fewer people had jobs when Reagan left office than when he became President.

5. Read "International Events." Then complete the statement.

Saddam Hussein invaded Kuwait so he could _____

_____

Practice Book
147 Use with *United States: Civil War to Today*, pp. 382–385

Vocabulary and Study Guide

Vocabulary

Write the definition of each vocabulary word below.

1. deregulation _____

2. deficit _____

_____

3. coalition _____

4. Use two of the words in a sentence.

_____

_____

Study Guide

Read "Reagan Becomes President." Then answer the questions below.

5. What changes did Ronald Reagan make in government spending?

_____

_____

6. What led to the largest U.S. budget deficit in the 1980s?

_____

_____

Event	Why it happened	Outcome
The end of the Cold War	7.	8.
The Persian Gulf War	9.	10.

Summary: New Technologies

Clinton's Presidency

In 1992, Bill Clinton was elected President. He believed government money should be used to help people. There was not enough money because of the budget deficit from the 1980s. The economy grew and more taxes were collected. Clinton put more money into social programs. By 1998, the United States had a budget surplus. The government had collected more money than it spent.

Clinton helped start peace processes in Northern Ireland and the Middle East. In the former country of Yugoslavia, different groups fought to form separate nations. The United States and other countries sent troops to try to stop the fighting there in the 1990s.

Clinton's second term was hurt by a scandal. He was impeached by the House of Representatives. The Senate found him not guilty.

A Changing Economy

During the 1990s, the United States had the longest period of economic growth in its history. Many people had more income to save, spend, or invest. Changes in computers and the development of high-tech businesses helped the economy grow and be more productive. Computer programs were invented that people could use at home, at school, and at work. The Internet made it possible for people to get information, shop, and communicate quickly and easily.

New technology made the U.S. economy more productive. Jobs changed with the economy. More people did service jobs. Some companies moved factories overseas where they could make products at a lower cost. People with more education did better in the 1990s than people with less education.

A Connected World

Improved communication and transportation made trade between countries less expensive and brought people closer. Nations are now more interdependent. Mexico, Canada, and the United States signed a free-trade agreement in the 1990s.

Before You Read

Find and underline each vocabulary word.

Internet *noun*, links computers around the world with each other

high-tech *adjective*, or high technology, uses the most recent knowledge and equipment

free-trade agreement *noun*, a treaty between countries that trade with each other

After You Read

REVIEW In which places did President Clinton help settle conflicts? Circle the names of three places where President Clinton helped settle conflicts.

REVIEW What effect did computers have on the economy in the 1990s? Circle the sentence that answers the question.

REVIEW In what ways did improvements in transportation and communication change life during the 1990s? Highlight the sentence that tells you the answer.

Practice Book
Use with *United States: Civil War to Today*, pp. 388–393

ame _____ Date _____

Reading Skill and Strategy

Reading Skill: Categorize

This skill helps you understand and remember what you have read by organizing facts into groups, or categories.

Read "A Changing Economy." Then fill in the category chart below. How did the economy change in the 1990s?

Computers	High-tech business	Jobs
1.	2.	3.

Reading Strategy: Monitor/Clarify

4. Read "Clinton's Presidency." Then complete the statement.

President Clinton started peace talks in _____

_____.

5. Read "A Changing Economy." Then explain the concept of high-tech business.

_____

_____

_____

Vocabulary and Study Guide

Vocabulary

1. Draw a line connecting the vocabulary word to its meaning.

Internet	a system that links computers around the world
high-tech	a treaty that removes trading taxes
free-trade agreement	the most recent knowledge and equipment

Study Guide

2. Read "Clinton's Presidency." Then fill in the blanks below.

When Bill Clinton first became President, there was a budget

_____. Then the economy started to grow. By 1998, the

government had a budget _____. President Clinton acted

as a _____ in Northern Ireland and the Middle East.

During his second term, he was accused of lying in court about his

private life and was _____. Later, the Senate found him

_____.

Read "A Changing Economy." Then fill in the causes-and-effect chart below.

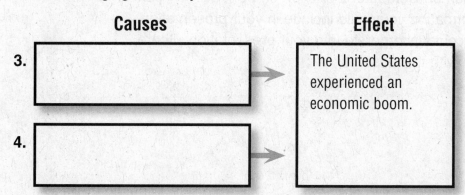

Causes	Effect
3.	The United States experienced an economic boom.
4.	

Skillbuilder: Create a Multimedia Presentation

Practice

1. What are two things you could include in a multimedia presentation about how television has changed over the years?

   _____

   _____

   _____

2. If you are going to make a multimedia presentation about the presidency of Bill Clinton, what is the first thing you should do?

   _____

   _____

3. Which media tools could you use to create a multimedia presentation about how better forms of transportation have increased trade between countries?

   _____

   _____

   _____

Apply

Create your own multimedia presentation about the evolution of cellular phones. Use the information on Computer Evolution on pp. 390–391 as a model for the kinds of information you could include in your presentation. Think of other media you could incorporate into your presentation. Share your finished presentation with the class.

Use with *United States: Civil War to Today*, pp. 394–395

Summary: Twenty-First Century Begins

The 2000 Election

On December 31, 1999, people all over the world celebrated the beginning of a new millennium. The new millennium really began on January 1, 2001. In a presidential election, the vote of individual citizens is called the popular vote. The candidate who wins the popular vote in a state wins all of that state's Electoral College votes. To win the election, you have to win the electoral vote.

The 2000 presidential election was an example of a very close popular and electoral vote. Whoever won the vote in Florida would win the election. In Florida, Bush won the first count. Gore said the votes were not counted properly. Finally, the Supreme Court said that the Florida votes would not be recounted. Bush became President.

The War on Terror

On September 11, 2001, nearly three thousand people were killed by acts of terrorism in the United States. Terrorists hijacked four airplanes. They crashed two airplanes into the World Trade Center in New York City, and one into the Pentagon in Washington, D.C. A fourth plane crashed in Pennsylvania.

The terrorists were from a group called al-Qaeda. Their leader was Osama bin Laden. They were against the United States' involvement in the Middle East. Osama bin Laden's headquarters was in Afghanistan. In October 2001, a coalition of nations led by the United States went to war in Afghanistan. The coalition won but they did not find bin Laden. The United States also created the Department of Homeland Security in 2002 to fight terrorism.

In 2003, Saddam Hussein was in power in Iraq. In March, 2003, the United States went to war in Iraq. After defeating Hussein's army and capturing Hussein, the military stayed in Iraq while a new Iraqi government formed.

Before You Read

Find and underline each vocabulary word.

millennium *noun*, a period of 10 centuries, or 1,000 years

popular vote *noun*, the vote of individuals

Electoral College *noun*, representatives, called electors, from each state who vote for the President and Vice President

terrorism *noun*, the use of violence against ordinary people to achieve a political goal

After You Read

REVIEW **What is the difference between the popular vote and the electoral vote?** Circle the words that tell what a popular vote is. Highlight the words that tell what the votes in the Electoral College are. Underline the words that explain how a presidential election is won.

REVIEW **How did the United States respond to the terrorist attacks of September 11, 2001?** Circle three sentences that tell you the answer.

Use with *United States: Civil War to Today*, pp. 396–399

Reading Skill and Strategy

Reading Skill: Cause and Effect

This skill helps you see how one event can be related to another, either by causing it or resulting from it.

Read "The War on Terror." Then fill in the cause-and-effect chart below to show the effect of the terrorist attacks on the United States.

| Al-Qaeda terrorists crashed two planes into the World Trade Center in New York City. | Al-Qaeda terrorists crashed a third plane into the Pentagon and hijacked a fourth plane that crashed in Pennsylvania. |

1. _____

Reading Strategy: Monitor/Clarify

Read "Twenty-First Century Begins." For each heading, write a sentence about that section.

2. Heading 1: The 2000 Election

_____

_____

3. Heading 2: The War on Terror

_____

_____

Vocabulary and Study Guide

Vocabulary

Across
3. vote of individuals
4. period of 10 centuries, or 1,000 years

Down
1. the _____ College
2. the use of violence against ordinary people to achieve a political goal

Study Guide

5. Read "The 2000 Election." Then fill in the blanks below.

The candidates in the 2000 presidential election were

_____ and _____. The presidential

election has two steps. The first step is the _____.

The next step is the Electoral College. The candidate who wins a state's

popular vote wins all of that state's Electoral College votes. To become

President, a candidate must win the _____ vote.

In Florida, the popular vote was so close that there was a disagreement,

and the _____ became involved.

6. Read "The War on Terror." Then fill in the blanks below.

On _____, terrorists attacked the United States

in New York City, Pennsylvania, and _____. Nearly

3,000 people were killed. The terrorists had their headquarters

in _____. The United States led a coalition of nations

into war in Afghanistan to capture their leader, _____.

The coalition won the war, but did not capture bin Laden.

Summary: United States Today

A Nation of Immigrants

Millions of immigrants come to the United States. Some come for a better life, and some come for religious or political freedom. Until 1965, most immigrants came from Europe or Mexico. In 1965, Congress changed the immigration laws. Now immigrants come from many nations. Spanish-speaking immigrants come from Central and South America and the Caribbean. Refugees from wars in El Salvador and Nicaragua come.

People also come from Africa and the West Indies. Today about one-third of America's immigrants are Asians from countries such as India, China, and the Philippines. Immigrants often live in communities where other people from their country live. They influence the culture and government of the places where they live.

Many People, One Nation

Many immigrants to the United States find the freedom they need to start successful careers. The United States has a diverse population, with many different ethnic groups. People bring music, food, language, art, and customs from their countries. Each person brings knowledge, skills, and talents. These things improve the United States. Ethnic diversity is one of the greatest strengths of the United States.

All people in the United States share a heritage of democracy. All United States citizens share the Constitution and the Bill of Rights. Our democratic heritage unites us into one nation. You can see the Latin motto "E pluribus unum" on American money. These Latin words mean "out of many, one." These words remind us that the United States became one nation by joining together 13 colonies. Today, 50 states and many ethnic groups are joined together into one nation.

Before You Read

Find and underline each vocabulary word.

refugee *noun,* a person who escapes war or other danger and seeks safety in another country

culture *noun,* the way of life a people create for themselves and pass on to their children

heritage *noun,* something that is passed down from one generation to the next

motto *noun,* a short statement that explains an ideal or a goal

After You Read

 REVIEW Why did immigration to the United States change after 1965? Circle the sentence that tells the answer.

REVIEW What do all U.S. citizens share? Draw a box around the sentence that tells the answer.

Reading Skill and Strategy

Reading Skill: Cause and Effect

This skill helps you see how one event can be related to another, either by causing it or resulting from it.

Read "A Nation of Immigrants." Then fill in the cause-and-effect chart below to show one effect of foreign wars on immigration.

Cause	Effect
There were wars in El Salvador and Nicaragua during the 1980s. →	1.

Reading Strategy: Summarize

2. Read "A Nation of Immigrants." Then check the statement that best summarizes the section.

   _____ Most immigrants want to live in Texas, California, or Florida.

   _____ Today, immigrants from many different countries move to the United States.

   _____ All immigrants to the United States are refugees who are seeking safety.

3. Read "Many People, One Nation." Then complete the summary.

   The many different ethnic groups living in the United States

   add to American culture with their _____

   _____

   _____

Practice Book
157 Use with *United States: Civil War to Today*, pp. 404–407

Vocabulary and Study Guide

Vocabulary

Solve the clue and write the answer in the blank. Then find the word in the puzzle. Look up, down, forward, and backward. Look for bonus words!

1. "E pluribus unum" is an example. _____

2. A person who escapes war or other danger and seeks safety in another country _____

3. Something that is passed down from one generation to the next _____

4. The way of life a people create for themselves and pass on to their children _____

Bonus Words: nation, people

E	R	A	P	O	Y	S	E
S	E	I	N	M	T	E	R
E	N	G	O	U	M	G	U
L	A	T	U	O	O	A	T
P	T	I	T	F	L	T	L
O	F	C	V	I	E	I	U
E	C	N	I	V	O	R	C
P	U	O	Z	W	M	E	K
N	O	I	T	A	N	H	B

Study Guide

5. Read "A Nation of Immigrants." Then fill in the blanks below.

Some immigrants come to the United States to escape

_____ or to have a safer and freer life.

Most early _____ came from Europe and

_____. New immigration laws in 1965 made it

easier for people to immigrate from Latin America, Africa, the

West Indies, and _____. Many immigrants settle

in _____ with people from their home country.

6. Read "Many People, One Nation." Then fill in the blanks below.

Most immigrants work hard because they hope to become

_____ in the United States. Their talents help

_____ the country in many ways. Ethnic and

religious _____ may be one of the United States'

greatest strengths. But all U.S. Citizens, no matter where they are

from, are united by a _____ heritage.

Skillbuilder: Resolve Conflicts

Read how the students in Ms. Lopez's class had to compromise while planning a party. Then answer the questions about how their conflict was resolved.

> The students in Ms. Lopez's class were planning a party to celebrate their different cultures. Each student wanted to bring food and music from his or her own culture. However, if each student brought one food and one song, there would be too much food to eat and not enough time to play all the music. The class decided to compromise by drawing straws. Half of the students would get to bring their favorite foods, and the other half would each bring one favorite song. In this way, all the cultures would be represented and everyone would be happy.

Practice

1. What was the conflict between the students? _____

_____

_____

2. How were their goals similar? _____

_____

_____

3. In what way was the solution a compromise? _____

_____

_____

Apply

Use your library or the Internet to research a time when Congress has had to come to a compromise over an issue that was different from immigration. Identify the conflict and the goals of each side that had to compromise. Then write a paragraph evaluating the success of the compromise.

Use with *United States: Civil War to Today*, pp. 410–411

Summary: Tennessee Traditions

The People of Tennessee

The population of Tennessee is about six million people. Most of the ancestors of the people of Tennessee came from Europe or Africa. The Cherokee are the largest group of American Indians. There is also a growing Latino and Asian population.

In the past, most Tennesseans made their living farming. Today, many people work in the service industries such as education, health care or business. Other people work in manufacturing.

Music has been an important part of Tennessee's culture for many years. The blues grew out of songs that had been sung by enslaved African Americans as they worked. These songs, that were often sad, helped them express their feelings and get their work done. Bessie Smith recorded one of the first blues records. She was known as the "Empress of the Blues."

Country music grew out of the folk music of the Appalachian Mountains. Bluegrass is a type of country music made popular by Bill Monroe and the Blue Grass Boys. Tennessee is also famous for its musicians, such as Elvis Presley and Dolly Parton. Tennessee is also home to writers, such as James Agee, and poets, such as Nikki Giovanni.

Tennessee Celebrations

Tennesseans celebrate their culture and traditions through festivals. The Beale Street Music Festival in Memphis and the Riverbend Festival in Chattanooga are two examples of music festivals. The Smoky Mountain Fiddlers Convention held each year is the biggest bluegrass music event in the Great Smoky Mountains.

People from all over the country and the world attend The Tennessee Walking Horse National Celebration. This celebration includes horse shows, concerts, and many other events. The Pioneer Day event in late summer features craft demonstrations and storytelling as well as music.

Before You Read

Find and underline each vocabulary word.

blues *noun*, music that grew out of songs that had been sung by enslaved African Americans as they worked

country music *noun*, music that grew out of the folk music of the Appalachian Mountains

bluegrass *noun*, a kind of country music introduced by the Grand Ole Opry

walking horse *noun*, a horse born with the ability to walk very quickly

After You Read

REVIEW **Who was Bessie Smith?** Circle the sentences that tell the answer.

REVIEW **What are some Tennessee customs and traditions that festivals celebrate?** Highlight the customs and traditions that festivals celebrate.

Reading Skill and Strategy

Reading Skill: Classify

This skill helps you remember what you have read by organizing facts into groups, or categories.

Read "Tennessee Celebrations." Then fill in the categorization chart below with names of Tennessee celebrations.

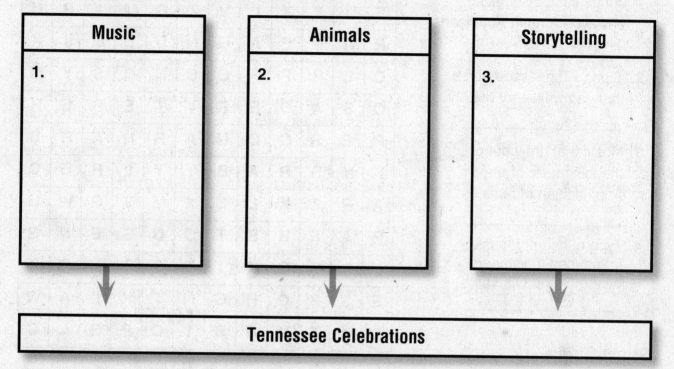

Reading Strategy: Summarize

4. Read "The People of Tennessee." Then check the statement that best summarizes the selection.

    _____ About one fourth of the people living in Tennessee were born there.

    _____ Tennesseans come from different backgrounds and most provide services or work in manufacturing.

    _____ Today most people in Tennessee earn their living by farming.

5. Read "Tennessee and the Arts." Then complete the summary.

    Music, such as _____, has been

    an important part of Tennessee culture, and Tennessee is home to

    famous authors, such as _____.

Practice Book
161   Use with *United States: Civil War to Today*, pp. 412–415

Vocabulary and Study Guide

Vocabulary

Solve the clue and write the answer in the blank. Then find the word in the puzzle. Look up, down, forward, and backward.

1. Music that grew out of songs sung by working enslaved African Americans

   _____

2. Type of Tennessee horse that can walk very quickly

   _____

3. Music that grew out of the folk music of the Appalachian Mountains

   _____

4. Type of country music introduced to listeners by the Grand Ole Opry

   _____

K	F	H	O	Q	B	I	C	S	V	O	T
E	J	Y	X	L	V	Z	O	M	I	P	U
R	W	H	E	A	G	N	U	L	T	J	K
C	L	R	P	F	O	U	N	C	S	Y	M
O	S	A	O	E	R	V	T	E	S	L	R
R	E	S	G	Q	N	A	R	H	A	R	S
K	M	S	R	A	B	Y	Y	L	R	E	C
A	R	Z	K	L	L	X	M	V	G	W	U
R	A	F	U	S	T	O	U	S	E	N	G
N	T	E	G	K	I	T	S	E	U	G	K
E	S	R	O	H	G	N	I	K	L	A	W
L	Y	T	M	A	S	I	C	P	B	L	C

Study Guide

Read "Tennessee and the Arts." Then fill in the cause-and-effect chart below.

Causes

5. [   ] →

Enslaved African Americans sang as they worked. → 6.

Radio shows like the Grand Ole Opry began broadcasting. → 7.

Effects

The pioneers brought folk songs and the fiddle from the British Isles.

6. [   ]

7. [   ]

Use with *United States: Civil War to Today,* pp. 412–415